THE STRUCTURE AND EVOLUTION
OF THE UNIVERSE

The Structure and Evolution of the Universe

AN INTRODUCTION TO COSMOLOGY

G. J. WHITROW

M.A., D.PHIL., F.R.A.S.

*Reader in Applied Mathematics in the University of London
at the Imperial College of Science and Technology, formerly
Lecturer of Christ Church, Oxford*

HARPER TORCHBOOKS / Science Library

HARPER & BROTHERS, PUBLISHERS

NEW YORK

A HARPER TORCHBOOK Original, first published 1959

TO MY WIFE

CONTENTS

ILLUSTRATIONS

PLATES
(Between pages 128 and 129)

FIGURES IN THE TEXT

PREFACE

In 1949 my book *The Structure of the Universe* was published by the Hutchinson University Library. Since then the book has been translated into Spanish, French and Italian. Two editions have been published, in 1952 and 1956, of the Spanish translation in the series *Brevarios del Fondo de Cultura Economica* (Mexico and Buenos Aires). The French translation (with additional notes) by Dr. Gérard de Vaucouleurs appeared in 1955 in the series *L'Avenir de la Science* (Gallimard, Paris). The Italian translation has been published in the series *Panorami Scientifici* (Longanesi, Milan).

When a second edition of the English text was called for recently, it soon became evident that the many and profound advances which had occurred in the intervening years necessitated a complete rewriting of almost the entire book. Consequently, the present text differs so greatly from the original that some modification of title is needed to indicate that this is essentially a new book.

I should like to take this opportunity to thank those friends, in particular Professor W. M. Smart and Dr. de Vaucouleurs, who were good enough to draw my attention to *errata* in the first edition of the book. In the preparation of the manuscript of the present book and index, and in the removal of obscurities of expression, the assistance of my wife has been, as always, invaluable.

I am also grateful to Sir George Thomson, F.R.S., for the interest he has shown in this book and for his advice.

G. J. W.

1

THE DEPTHS OF THE UNIVERSE (1)

'LET man then contemplate the whole of nature in her full and grand mystery, and turn his vision from the low objects which surround him. Let him gaze on that brilliant light, set like an eternal lamp to illumine the universe; let the earth appear to him a point in comparison with the vast circle described by the sun, and let him wonder at the fact that this vast circle is itself but a very fine point in comparison with that described by the stars in their revolution round the firmament. But if our view be arrested there let our imagination pass beyond; it will sooner exhaust the power of conception than nature that of supplying material for conception. The whole visible world is only an imperceptible atom in the ample bosom of nature. No idea approaches it. We may enlarge our conceptions beyond all imaginable space; we only produce atoms in comparison with the reality of things. It is an infinite sphere, the centre of which is everywhere, the circumference nowhere.' So wrote the great French mathematician Pascal three hundred years ago.

For centuries innumerable, men had imagined the whole physical universe to be enclosed in a *finite* sphere. The Sun and Moon and the five planets were the principal heavenly bodies, to each of which was ascribed a special domain in which it traced its path. By an elaborate and ingenious theory their observed motions were adequately described in terms of epicycles, or circles whose centres revolve on other circles. In the background was the spinning sphere of stars, for these were all supposed to be at the same distance from the Earth, the hub of the universe.

When Pascal wrote, faith in this simple picture of the world was being undermined by one of the most momentous revolutions which have occurred in the history of thought. Much had happened in the previous hundred years to cause men to question their former ideas.

The old scholastic teachings of the universities had degenerated into futile logomachies, and the more alert minds had turned away from the fixed mediaeval order of nature to humanism with its less rigid and more relativistic point of view. In the world of trade and travel men were also becoming conscious of wider horizons. After the famous voyages of Henry the Navigator, Columbus and Magellan, it no longer seemed that the only centre of importance in the world was Europe. Furthermore, the Reformation had shaken the old belief that there was a unique religious centre. The rise of Protestantism, with its emphasis on personal faith, was perhaps the most powerful disruptive influence, but also in art and letters there was a tendency to nationalism which favoured the idea that there was no one fixed centre of the world.

Into this explosive mental atmosphere an obscure Polish cleric launched a thunderbolt. In his *De Revolutionibus Orbium Caelestium*, published in 1543, Copernicus suggested that the Earth was not the unique centre of the astronomical universe, any more than Jerusalem or Rome was the centre of the habitable region of the Earth. He argued that the mathematical description of the observed motions of the heavenly bodies could be simplified if the Earth was regarded no longer as fixed and if all motion was depicted as being relative to the sphere of the fixed stars, at the centre of which he placed the Sun. His argument was mainly mathematical, but he pointed out that, if it were objected that a moving Earth would fly to pieces, then *a fortiori* a moving crystalline sphere of stars, rotating at a far greater rate, would be even more likely to disintegrate. The daily rotation of the heavens was thus transferred to the Earth.

The next advance was made by Thomas Digges in 1576, and also by the famous Giordano Bruno whose restless imagination could no longer be content with the idea that the stars outside the solar system were enclosed in a shell concentric with either the Earth or the Sun. A serious objection raised against the Copernican system was that, if the Earth revolved about the Sun, then in the course of the year there should be a distinct annual change in the apparent positions of the stars relative to the Earth. As such an annual motion or parallax, as it is usually called, was not observed, the only answer which the upholders of the new theory could offer was that the stars were immensely distant compared with the planets.

We have seen that, in referring to the stellar realm beyond the planets, Pascal remarked, 'if our view be arrested there let our imagination pass beyond'. Despite the invention of the telescope and its application to astronomical observation early in the seventeenth century by Galileo, the region of the stars was not explored until long after Pascal wrote. The stars were seen merely as a framework bounding the region in which the astronomer could conduct his investigations. Whether the stars were all at the same distance, or whether they were scattered throughout infinite space, or whether they formed a finite system of vast but limited depth, were questions that could not be answered until towards the end of the eighteenth century. Until then stellar astronomy was a field left to the unaided imagination.

Due to the genius and labours of Newton (1642–1727), almost all the problems presented by the motions of the planets had been mastered. Newton had shown for all time that these motions could be completely accounted for if it were assumed that the same laws of nature, and in particular gravity, operated in the celestial realm as well as in the terrestrial. Although the old Aristotelian distinction between the corrupt Earth and the incorruptible heavens was thus finally abandoned, the stellar realm still lay beyond the range of scientific investigation. The natural step, taken by Digges and Bruno, of likening the stars to the Sun and scattering them throughout space was still only a step of the imagination.

Copernicus made his revolutionary suggestion on purely theoretical grounds. The invention of the telescope came after, and not before, the publication of his great work. This is a fact on which we may well ponder, for it shows that insight into natural phenomena has come as much from the genius of the theoretical as from that of the experimental and observational investigator.

However, the next significant advance in the growth of our conception of the universe was due to one of the greatest observational astronomers of all time, William Herschel (1738–1822). By profession a musician, Herschel came to this country from Hanover where he had been a bandsman in the Foot Guards. He made rapid progress in the musical profession, and in 1766 was appointed organist of the Octagon Chapel at Bath. This post he held for sixteen years, but all his spare time was devoted to optics and astronomy.

Too poor to afford a telescope but, to quote his own words, 'resolved to take nothing upon trust but to see with my own eyes all that other men had seen before', he finally decided to make a telescopic mirror for himself. By the spring of 1774, after two hundred failures, he constructed his first reflecting telescope, and within seven years made one of the most sensational discoveries in the history of astronomy: the first planetary discovery since prehistoric times, Uranus. Herschel's success was due to his ability to construct better telescopes than had ever been made before, to the keenness of his vision ('seeing is in some respects an art which must be learnt') and above all to his genius.

The greatest enterprise of Herschel's life was his attempt to map the stellar regions beyond the solar system. Significantly, the first problem which he attacked was that of stellar parallax. This is the problem of determining the apparent angular displacement in the sky of a given star in the course of the Earth's journey from one point of its orbit round the Sun to the diametrically opposite point. The discovery of Uranus was a chance by-product of this investigation. As Uranus is about twice as far from the Sun as Saturn, the next nearest planet, Herschel's discovery incidentally doubled the known extent of the solar system; but, from Herschel's point of view, its most important consequence was that he came under royal patronage. George III created for him the post of King's Astronomer with a salary of £200 a year. This enabled him to abandon music and devote his time and energy entirely to astronomy and above all to his great project of a systematic survey of the heavens.

Herschel was the pioneer of modern statistical astronomy. He instituted 'star gauges' or counts of the number of stars visible in his telescope in different parts of the sky, and two great problems emerged therefrom. One was the problem of determining the Sun's own motion among the stars, and the other was the investigation of the shape and structure of the Milky Way, or Galaxy, which Galileo had found early in the seventeenth century to be composed of a vast number of faint stars.

In 1718 the great British astronomer Halley discovered that the positions of three bright stars—Sirius, Arcturus and Aldebaran—differed appreciably from their positions as recorded in the catalogue compiled by Hipparchus nearly two thousand years before, due

allowance being made for the effect of the precession of the equi-
noxes, or top-like motion of the Earth's axis of rotation. The obvious
explanation of this phenomenon was that the three stars had moved
at right angles to the line of sight against the general background of
the other stars. The first breach was thus made in the age-old conception that the stars were fixed, but little progress was made before
Herschel. His earliest paper in 1783 is largely devoted to a philosophical attempt to prove that, as the Sun is a star, it too should
move against the background of the stars as a whole.

'If the proper motion of the stars in general be at once admitted,'
asked Herschel, 'who can refuse to allow that our Sun, with its
planets and comets, is no less liable to such a general agitation as we
find to obtain among all the rest of the celestial bodies?' He argued
that the Sun's motion could only be detected by a general drift of
the stars in a contrary direction, those stars ahead of the Sun appearing to disperse, while those behind tend to draw together. The determination of the solar motion, however, is complicated by the fact
that the stars themselves have their own proper motions. Thus the
observed motion of each star would have to be decomposed into two
component factors, the star's own motion and the reflection of the
Sun's motion in the opposite direction.

In his first paper Herschel tentatively fixed the direction of the
Sun's motion as being towards a point in the constellation Hercules,
near the star Lambda Herculis. Moreover, although very few proper
motions were known with accuracy and no one had yet succeeded in
measuring the distance of a single star, in his second paper in 1806
Herschel advanced an estimate for the amount of solar motion,
which he expressed in terms of the then unknown distance of Sirius.
Using the now accepted value for the latter, his result was fourteen
kilometres per second as compared with the modern value of
twenty kilometres per second.

The other main problem which engaged Herschel's attention was
the general distribution of the stars. In two papers, presented to the
Royal Society in 1785, he put forward the first definite model of the
stellar system. He determined the relative distances of stars in 3,400
regions of known position on the assumption that all stars were of
the same absolute brightness, so that apparent brightness became his
criterion of relative distance. We now know that this is an extremely

poor criterion for individual stars; statistically it is more satisfactory, and it was of course in this way that Herschel used it and thereby came to the conclusion that there are a finite number of stars, according to his data from 75 to 100 million. These are grouped in a bun-shaped system, the appearance of the Milky Way in the sky being an optical effect due to this shape. He estimated the diameter of the Galaxy, as we now call the system, to be 850 times and the thickness to be 155 times the average distance of a first magnitude star, such as Sirius. He believed that the Sun was placed near but not quite at the centre, a result which more recent research has since modified considerably. On the other hand, his belief that the Sun is very near the central plane, because the Milky Way appears to divide the sky into two almost exactly equal parts, has been entirely confirmed.

This conception of a stellar system isolated in space appears to have been first put forward as a possible hypothesis by an English instrument maker, Thomas Wright, in 1750. But his speculations did not rest there. As Hubble has so pertinently remarked, the few speculations on the general structure of the universe which have survived the results of observational exploration have all been based on the principle of uniformity—that, in a general sense, any sample of the universe is much like any other sample. In accordance with this principle, Wright found the conception of a finite system of stars isolated in infinite Euclidean space unsatisfactory. As the idea of finite non-Euclidean space had not then been invented, he suggested that there exist other systems similar to the Galaxy, just as the stars are other bodies similar to the Sun. Five years later the great German philosopher Immanuel Kant developed this conception further. Some of Kant's remarks have been cited by Hubble, in a rather free translation, as an excellent example of reasonable speculation based on the principle of uniformity.

'Let us imagine a system of stars gathered together in a common plane, like those of the Milky Way, but situated so far away from us that even with the telescope we cannot distinguish the stars composing it; let us assume that its distance, compared to that separating us from the stars of the Milky Way, is in the same proportion as the distance of the Milky Way is to the distance from the earth to the Sun; such a stellar world will appear to the observer, who contemplates it at so enormous a distance, only as a feeble spot feebly illumined and subtending a very small angle; its shape will be circular, if its plane is perpendicular to the line of sight, elliptical, if it is seen obliquely. The faintness of its light, its form, and its appreciable diameter will obviously distinguish such a phenomenon from the isolated stars around it.

'We do not need to seek far in the observations of the astronomers to meet with such phenomena. They have been seen by various observers, who have wondered at their strange appearance, have speculated upon them, and have suggested sometimes the most amazing explanations, sometimes theories which were more rational, but which had no more foundation than the former. We refer to the nebulae, or, more precisely, to a particular kind of celestial body which M. de Maupertuis describes as follows: "These are small luminous patches, only slightly more brilliant than the dark background of the sky; they have this in common, that their shapes are more or less open ellipses; and their light is far more feeble than that of any other objects to be perceived in the heavens. . . ."

'It is much more natural and reasonable to assume that a nebula is not a unique and solitary sun, but a system of numerous suns, which appear crowded, because of their distance, into a space so limited that their light, which would be imperceptible were each of them isolated, suffices, owing to their enormous numbers, to give a pale and uniform lustre. Their analogy with our own system of stars; their form, which is precisely what it should be according to our theory; the faintness of their light, which denotes an infinite distance; all are in admirable accord and lead us to consider these elliptical spots as systems of the same order as our own—in a word, to be Milky Ways similar to the one whose constitution we have explained. And if these hypotheses, in which analogy and observation consistently lend mutual support, have the same merit as formal demonstrations, we must consider the existence of such systems as demonstrated. . . .

'We see that scattered throughout space out to infinite distances there exist similar systems of stars, and that creation, in the whole extent of its infinite grandeur, is everywhere organized into systems whose members are in relation with one another. . . . A vast field lies open to discoveries, and observation alone will give the key.'

These remarkable speculations found their first substantial observational support in the investigations of Herschel, who made a systematic search for nebulae. In 1783 Messier catalogued 103 such objects which are still known by the numbers he assigned to them. For example, the famous nebula in Andromeda is M31. In striking confirmation of Kant's hypothesis, Herschel found that a number of these 'nebulae' were resolved into stars by his telescope. These 'nebulae' are in fact now called *globular clusters*,[1] forming parts of, or adjuncts to, the Galaxy rather than totally independent and comparable systems. Others, however, appeared to be just beyond his telescope's power of resolution. On calculating the minimum distance at which they must therefore be, Herschel concluded that 'the stupendous sidereal system we inhabit, consisting of many millions of stars, is, in all probability, a detached nebula. Among the great number of nebulae which I have now already seen, amounting to more than 900, there are many which in all probability are equally extensive with that which we inhabit.'

The problem of confirming such speculations was laborious and difficult. Indeed, in later years Herschel modified his views considerably. In 1811 he wrote: 'I must freely confess that by continuing my sweep of the heavens my opinion of the arrangement of the stars and their magnitudes, and of some other particulars, has undergone a gradual change. . . . We may also have surmised nebulae to be no other than clusters of stars disguised by their very great distance, but a longer experience and better acquaintance with the nature of nebulae will not allow a general admission of such a principle.'

In his early papers in 1785 Herschel had assumed an approximately equal scattering of stars in the Galaxy, for although 'in all probability there may not be two or three of them in the heavens, whose mutual distance shall be equal to that of any other two given stars, but it should be considered that when we take all the stars collectively there will be a mean distance which may be assumed as the general one'. However, by 1802 he fully recognized that 'this immense starry aggregation is by no means uniform. The stars of which it is composed are very unequally scattered, and show evident marks of clustering together into many separate allotments.' He

[1] For a modern photograph of a typical globular cluster, *see* Plate II.

thus came to regard the Galaxy as a system consisting of many local groups and clusters, and then to question the complete universality of his original view that all nebulae are distant 'island universes' comparable to our own galactic system. By 1811 Herschel had foreseen the modern division of nebulae into two classes of objects, the one consisting of external galaxies and the other of diffuse matter within our own galaxy, for example the nebulous mass in Orion, which he concluded was comparatively close to us, in agreement with present-day opinion.

The problem of the nature and status of the nebulae was, in fact, one of the most difficult which Herschel tackled, because he had no direct knowledge of the distances of a single object outside the solar system. In 1785, supposing them all to be unresolved aggregations of stars, he thrust them all outside the Galaxy, thus imagining he had pierced through the boundaries of the Milky Way, but by 1817 he admitted that 'the utmost stretch of the space-penetrating power of the 20-foot telescope could not fathom the profundity of the Milky Way'. Besides the existence of unresolved nebulae, the fact that with a 40-foot telescope he saw more stars than with a 20-foot telescope made it seem improbable that he had reached the confines of the universe; a background remained. Thus, although he still maintained his view that some of the distant nebulae were independent stellar systems, the evidence was most inconclusive. Consequently, as Eddington has remarked, 'the status of the nebulae has undergone remarkable vicissitudes'. In 1864 Sir William Huggins found that the light from the Orion nebula and from some others was similar to that emanating from a glowing mass of gas. This made it impossible to regard them as aggregations of stars, and so the observational evidence appeared to favour the view that all unresolved nebulae were masses of glowing gas within the Galaxy.

In addition to his vast pioneer work on the general structure of the sidereal universe, one further discovery by Herschel is of outstanding cosmological significance. For, just as by his systematic methods of star gauging he discovered that the speculations on the distribution of matter which had been based on the principle of uniformity were in essence correct, so by observing double stars he was the first to show that the laws of Nature holding outside the solar system conformed with those prevailing within. Newton's intellectual masterpiece was the discovery that planetary and terrestrial motion could be brought within the scope of the same law of gravitation; likewise, Herschel's greatest achievement was his brilliant demonstration that the same law governed the motion of stars. In 1802 he discovered evidence of orbital rotation in a number of double stars, and in 1804 he concluded beyond doubt that 'many doubles must be allowed to be real binary combinations of two stars intimately held together by the bond of mutual attraction'.

Well merited are the words of Sir William Herschel's epitaph in Upton Church, *Coelorum perrupit claustra*, for he broke through the barrier of the heavens and 'looked further into space than any human being ever did before him'. As Sir Oliver Lodge has reminded us, before Herschel's discoveries 'the stars had only been observed for nautical and practical purposes . . . they had been treated as a clock or piece of dead mechanism, and as fixed points of reference. All the energies of the astronomers had gone towards the solar system. It was the planets that had been observed. Tycho had observed and tabulated their positions. Kepler had found out some laws of their motion. Galileo had discovered their peculiarities and attendants. Newton and Laplace had perceived every detail of their laws. . . . But for the stars—the old Ptolemaic system might still have been true. They might still be mere dots in a vast crystalline sphere, all set at about one distance, and subservient to the uses of the Earth. . . . Herschel changed all this. Instead of sameness, he found variety; instead of uniformity of distance, limitless and utterly limitless fields and boundless distances; instead of rest and quiescence, motion and activity; instead of stagnation, life.'

One obvious criticism of Herschel's work was that it was based purely on data obtainable in England, so that all stars round the south celestial pole to within twenty degrees of the celestial equator were left out of account. To remedy this omission, his son, Sir John Herschel, transported a 20-foot telescope to South Africa in 1834. Within four years he succeeded in corroborating the general views of his father, although it appeared that the Sun was not so centrally situated within the Galaxy as he had imagined, being displaced somewhat towards the great star clouds forming its southern boundaries. The most remarkable result, however, of the younger Herschel's survey was the discovery that the nebulae, over seventeen hundred of which were catalogued and classified, tended to avoid the girdle of the Milky Way and to congregate most thickly towards the galactic poles, as the regions of the sky farthest away from this girdle are called.

The main criticism of William Herschel's pioneer investigations was that he had failed to discover the yard-stick of the universe, for he had no means other than plausible hypotheses for estimating the distance of a single star. As his whole conception of the sidereal universe turned on the assumption that the stars were at different distances, clearly the next step in the march of investigation must be the determination of these distances.

Although the classical theoretical foundation of distance measurement in physics is the 'rigid rod', nearly all distances in surveying, whether terrestrial or celestial, are made to depend on the properties of light. The two simplest properties so employed are the principle of propagation in straight lines and the principle that the intensity of light diminishes inversely as the square of the distance.[1]

The former is the basis of trigonometrical surveying. It was used in antiquity by Aristarchus to make the first scientific attempt to measure the size and distance of the Sun and Moon by considering the phenomena to be observed at an eclipse of the Moon and also when the Moon was half full. Although his methods were accurate in principle, the results he obtained were much too small, owing to the technical difficulty of measuring the necessary angles with sufficient accuracy. He arrived, however, at the revolutionary conclusion that the Sun was larger than the Earth, and that in modern measurement its distance was over four million miles, about one-twentieth of the true figure.

The latter property was used in the second half of the seventeenth century by Newton and by Huygens to estimate stellar distances. To obtain a first crude approximation, they assumed the Sun to be a star and also that all stars had the same absolute magnitude of brightness. Thus the apparent faintness of the stars was used to

[1] In Euclidean space the area of a sphere is proportional to the square of its radius and hence light that is radiated from a source equally in all directions will diminish in intensity according to the inverse square of the distance from the source.

obtain the general order of magnitude of their distances. For example, Huygens compared the light of Sirius with that of the reflection from a small sphere of glass of a small portion of the Sun's disc and found the star to be twenty-eight thousand times more distant than the Sun. This figure is about twenty times too small, partly because Sirius has since been found to be about twenty-five times as bright as the Sun and partly because Huygens' measurements were faulty. Similarly, Newton concluded that the average distance of the stars of the first magnitude was about thirty times Huygens' estimate for Sirius.

These first crude approximations revealed the enormous scale of the stellar universe compared with that of the solar system and also showed the inadequacy of existing technique to estimate stellar distances trigonometrically; for this method depends on measuring the parallax or apparent swinging motion of a star resulting from the Earth's orbital motion. Nevertheless, during the eighteenth century numerous attempts were made to measure this phenomenon, but in each case without success.

The key to the problem was the discovery, already noted, of stellar motion by Halley in 1718. More than a century later a German astronomer, Bessel, director of the Königsberg observatory, noted that a faint object, numbered 61 Cygni, i.e. 61 in the constellation of the Swan, had the fastest movement of any star then known, an interval of 300 years apparently sufficing to carry it across the sky through a distance equal to the diameter of the Moon. He concluded that such rapid angular motion relative to the general background of more distant stars (the technical term is *proper motion*) must be due to relative proximity, despite the object's apparent faintness.

Until then all attacks on the problem of stellar distance had been confined to the apparently brightest stars, but in December 1838 Bessel published his first results on the distance of this fainter star, making full use of the latest developments in observational technique and in the principles of optics. In the previous year Struve, who afterwards became the first director of the famous Pulkowa observatory near St. Petersburg, had detected the parallactic motion of the bright star Vega, but his results were not very consistent. Bessel's results, however, were; and his estimated distance of 61 Cygni as about 60 million million miles, or over half a million times as far away as the Sun, is now recognized to be the first reliable measurement of a star's distance, differing from the now accepted value by only a few per cent.

Two months later Henderson, then Astronomer Royal for Scotland, announced the result of observations on Alpha Centauri which he had made several years before at the Cape Observatory. These showed that it was about 20 million million miles away. Modern measurements have increased this figure by about thirty per cent., but this 'star' (it is actually a triple system) is still believed to be the nearest to the Sun. In the opinion of Professor Smart, if Henderson 'had discussed the Cape observations without unreasonable delay he would have had the distinction, so rightly adjudged to Bessel, of being the first to bridge successfully the vast gap between us and the stars'.

In 1840 Struve succeeded in measuring the distance of Vega. Although his result was about half that now accepted, the greater distance of this star made his achievement a remarkable one, for his task was equivalent to measuring the angle subtended by the diameter of a silver threepenny piece situated at a distance of about a dozen miles! Nevertheless, further progress was slow and disappointing until modern photographic methods were introduced at the beginning of the present century, following pioneer efforts by Pritchard at Oxford.

The scale of the stellar system is clearly one to which terrestrial units, e.g. the mile, are inappropriate. In practice, the two most convenient units of distance in stellar astronomy are the *light-year* and the *parsec*. The light-year is the distance travelled by light *in vacuo* in one year at the rate of about 186,000 miles or 300,000 kilometres per second, i.e. about 6 million million miles. The parsec[1] is the distance at which a star would exhibit a parallax of one second of arc (one thirty-six-hundredth of a degree). It is about three and a quarter light-years. Thus 61 Cygni is now estimated to be 11·1 light-years distant, and the nearest star about 4·3 light-years.

Herschel's memoirs on the structure of the universe were studied

----

[1] The terms *kiloparsec* (a thousand times the distance corresponding to one parsec) and *megaparsec* (a million times the same distance) are often used by astronomers when referring to very distant objects.

in great detail by Struve whose own researches led him to regard the whole system of stars, clusters and nebulae as of finite thickness but of infinite extension in the galactic plane. Herschel's original idea of a finite galaxy surrounded by other stellar systems or island universes thus fell further into disfavour. The discovery, already mentioned, that the unresolved nebulae tended to avoid the galactic plane appeared to be further evidence against the view that they were *independent* stellar systems, and during the remainder of the nineteenth and the first decade of the twentieth century the focal point of interest in cosmology was the general structure of the Galaxy.

The remarkable degree of success achieved by Herschel in elucidating the structure of the sidereal system, despite his ignorance of data concerning individual stars, was primarily due to his skill in devising and using statistical methods. These methods were greatly extended and elaborated between 1884 and 1911 by the German astronomer Seeliger who introduced the fruitful idea of a frequency distribution in the intrinsic brightness of the stars. This was a great advance over Herschel's assumption of uniform intrinsic brightness, for it came to be widely recognized that individual stars vary remarkably in their luminosity. Seeliger's idea was to count the number of stars between different ranges of apparent brightness, and not merely the total number, visible in different parts of the sky. Thus it was possible to determine the relative rate at which the stars fell off in number at increasing distances from the centre of the sidereal system. Seeliger's final model was a watch-shaped system similar to Herschel's, the star density decreasing with distance from the Sun. The estimated diameter was 7,250 parsecs or 23,000 light-years, about four times the figure assigned by Herschel, and the thickness nearly 6,000 light-years.

The statistical analysis of stellar distribution was refined by several astronomers and above all by the great Dutch astronomer Kapteyn who spent twelve years on the stupendous task of measuring and recording the positions and brightnesses of nearly half a million stars photographed in the southern hemisphere. This achievement appears all the more remarkable when we realize that the work was carried out practically single-handed in two small rooms borrowed from the physiological department of the University of Groningen, although at one time he had the help of a few convicts loaned to him from a Dutch prison.

The most important advance in method made by Kapteyn was his scheme of 'selected areas'. Since the number of stars in our Galaxy is probably of the order of a hundred thousand million it is clearly impossible to count more than a minute fraction. To obtain reliable results it is therefore of the utmost importance to select our samples fairly. As most of the data related to the brighter and hence more easily observed stars, Kapteyn proposed that 252 small regions of the sky distributed more or less evenly over the heavens be chosen and observatories all over the world be asked to co-operate in recording data concerning every star from the brightest to the faintest that could be observed in these regions. This scheme is still far from complete, but by fixing the limits of the Galaxy where the star density falls off to one-hundredth of its value near the Sun, Kapteyn obtained a distribution similar in shape to those of Herschel and Seeliger but with a diameter of 55,000 light-years or about nine times that assigned by Herschel, and a thickness of 11,000 light-years.

One feature of the Kapteyn system calls for immediate comment. In his model of the Galaxy, as in those of Herschel and Seeliger, the Sun still occupies a central position. The validity of this conception was open to question. The whole trend of astronomy since Copernicus had been against the previously prevailing idea that Man occupied a preferential position in the physical universe. As the Earth had been dethroned from its central position in the solar system, it was also felt that there was no reason why the Sun should be central in the Galaxy. Indeed, in view of the enormous number of stars, the probability was overwhelmingly against this concept.

Furthermore, it was realized that a very small amount of absorption of light, for example by diffuse material in interstellar space, would completely upset the calculated density distribution, and thus the results so laboriously achieved could only be regarded as provisional. Indeed, recent investigations have led us to believe that we live in a kind of celestial fog which is densest in and near the plane of the Milky Way. The effect of this obscuring matter is believed to be so great that light is halved in intensity after travelling about a thousand parsecs. It follows that the majority of the more distant objects in the Galaxy cannot be seen, and we are deceived into imagining that we are more centrally situated than in fact we are. Moreover, it is now realized that the distances formerly assigned to faint objects were probably too large, so that previous estimates of the dimensions of the sidereal system were excessive.

However, the principal cosmological significance of the existence of interstellar obscuring matter is that a new explanation is suggested for the fact that the nebulae appear to avoid the plane of the Milky Way. None are to be seen there, not because there are none in those directions, but because the general obscuration of light prevents our observing them. Thus the hypothesis that the nebulae must be satellite systems to the Galaxy is greatly weakened, because the mere fact that they shun the central plane can no longer be taken to indicate that they are influenced by it.

The crucial factor, however, in deciding between these rival speculations, and also in dethroning the Sun from its central position in the Kapteyn universe, was the discovery of a remarkable new astronomical yard-stick. Again our knowledge of the universe has been extended by a new application of the principle of the diminution of light intensity with the square of the distance. In 1912 Miss Leavitt, of the Harvard Observatory, found an empirical relation between the periods and luminosities of a certain type of variable star. These stars, known as Cepheids after their prototype Delta Cephei, when regularly observed yield a typical and easily recognized light fluctuation curve. There is a rapid increase of light, followed by a more gradual decline and then again by the same rapid increase and slow decline as before. Near the Galaxy is a particular system of stars known as the Lesser Magellanic Cloud. In this cloud there are a number of Cepheid variables, and Miss Leavitt discovered that the light of the brighter Cepheids fluctuated more slowly than the light of the fainter ones. Since the Magellanic Clouds are aggregations of very faint stars, it can be assumed for all practical purposes that these stars are equally distant, so that the relation between period of fluctuation and average apparent brightness can be interpreted as due to a relation between period and average intrinsic brightness.

The intrinsic brightness of a star is called its *luminosity* or *absolute magnitude*. To calculate this quantity for a particular star, we must first determine another quantity called its *apparent magnitude*. This is measured in terms of a scale of numbers which increase in arithmetical progression as the apparent brightnesses decrease in geometrical progression so that a difference of five magnitudes, e.g. between a star of the first magnitude and one of the sixth, signifies that the light received from the former is one hundred times that received from the latter. The scale extends to negative values, for example the apparent magnitude of the brightest star in the sky, Sirius, is $-1\cdot6$. Having determined the apparent magnitude of a star, we obtain its absolute magnitude by calculating what its apparent magnitude would be if the star were at a distance of ten parsecs ($32\cdot6$ light-years). This calculation is based on the law that apparent brightness diminishes inversely as the square of the distance. Thus, since the distance of Sirius is about $8\cdot6$ light-years its absolute magnitude is found to be $+13$.

If all Cepheid variables with the same period of light fluctuation have the same[1] average absolute magnitude, it follows that the ratio of the apparent magnitudes of any two Cepheids of the same period will depend solely on the ratio of their distances. Consequently, Miss Leavitt's discovery revealed the great importance of Cepheids as *distance-indicators*. The principal difficulty in using them for this purpose was to convert the scale of relative distances into an absolute scale. To do this it was essential to determine in some other way the actual distances of a few of the nearest Cepheids. Unfortunately, there is no Cepheid sufficiently close to the Sun for its parallax to be measured directly. Therefore, the distances to the nearest Cepheids had to be measured indirectly by a statistical method based on the determination of proper motions against the general background of more distant stars.[2]

It was then possible to compute the absolute magnitudes of these stars and hence to obtain the so-called *period-luminosity curve* correlating the periods of Cepheid variables with their mean absolute magnitudes. With this curve the distance of any Cepheid variable of known period could be determined by comparing its mean apparent

[1] *See*, however, page 48 for the latest views on this hypothesis.
[2] The reader who wishes to investigate this point further may like to consult H. Spencer Jones, *General Astronomy*, Section 215. Parallaxes determined by this method are known as *statistical parallaxes*.

magnitude with the mean absolute magnitude corresponding to this period.

This new method of estimating stellar distances was particularly valuable because it could be applied where other methods failed owing to the remoteness of the object concerned. It was used by the American astronomer Harlow Shapley to determine the distances of the globular clusters of stars surrounding the Milky Way. About a hundred of these clusters are known and they all look much alike (*see* Plate II) except for apparent size, and this is probably mainly due to differences of distance. Cepheid variables abound in them, and Shapley found that the distances of these clusters range from about 20,000 to about 200,000 light-years. At such distances the parallactic method of measuring distance would be hopelessly inapplicable; as Jeans has remarked, the parallactic orbit of a star at the distance of the furthest globular clusters is about equivalent to the size of a pin-head at the other side of the Atlantic.

From the cosmological aspect, the most significant result of Shapley's work was the discovery that the Sun is near one edge of the cluster system, the geometrical centre of which was found to be in the direction of Sagittarius where the star clouds are richest. When the clusters were plotted on a plane perpendicular to the central plane of the Milky Way and passing through the Sun and the centre of the globular system, it was found that they were symmetrically distributed. Assuming that this indicated some intimate connection between the stellar and globular systems, Shapley argued that the two were probably concentric. He thus estimated the Galaxy to have a diameter of about a quarter of a million light-years and a thickness of about 15,000 light-years, the Sun being at about 65,000 light-years from the centre. Shapley's model was therefore about five times as wide as Kapteyn's.

More recent work has tended to reduce these dimensions, which made no allowance for the effect of interstellar obscuring matter and were also based on the assumption that the effective boundary of the main stellar system is to be found in the region of the globular clusters. Thus, although the distance of the Sun from the centre of the Galaxy is still somewhat uncertain, it is now thought to be approximately 8,900 parsecs, roughly 30,000 light-years, i.e. less than half of Shapley's original estimate. The diameter of the Milky Way in the main plane is estimated to be about 80,000 light-years and its greatest thickness in the direction perpendicular to this plane is about one-fifth of the main diameter, but there is no sharp boundary in any direction. The diameter of the surrounding spherical halo of globular clusters is about 130,000 light-years. The total number of stars in the Galaxy is now believed to be of the order of a hundred thousand million.

2

THE DEPTHS OF THE UNIVERSE (II)

OUR ability to estimate the distance of any group of stellar objects in which Cepheid variables of known period and apparent brightness can be identified has found its most outstanding application in the solution of the old problem of the status of the nebulae. Herschel had originally placed them all outside the Galaxy, but later came to the conclusion that some were constituent members of this system. During the nineteenth century it was discovered that some nebulae were gaseous and definitely within the boundaries of the Galaxy. Other nebulae were found to have a peculiar structure.

In 1845 Lord Rosse completed his famous reflecting telescope, with a gigantic mirror six feet in diameter. Erected in a country district of Ireland, mainly with local labour, and with none of the advantages which are provided by modern tools, it was one of the greatest *tours de force* in the history of telescopic construction. It could not compete with modern instruments in exploring the depths of space, because these regions can only be studied satisfactorily by photographic methods using very long exposures. In 1845 these had not been invented, and in any case the telescope, owing to its mechanical and optical shortcomings, was not suited for their employment.

Nevertheless, with this huge but primitive instrument Lord Rosse made one of the capital discoveries of observational astronomy. Scarcely two months after its completion it was directed to the nebula M51, near the tail of the Great Bear. Sir John Herschel had previously depicted this nebula as a split ring surrounding a bright nucleus, but the 6-foot mirror yielded a very different picture. For the first time the famous spiral structure, lavishly employed by nature in the organic world, was revealed in the heavens. Nothing like it had ever been seen by any previous observer, but Lord Rosse ultimately catalogued fourteen nebulae of this particular shape. However, so faint are these objects that few more could be discovered until the advent of photographic methods. With improved telescopes and exposures of many hours, more and more have been revealed, and even before the construction of the 100-inch telescope at Mount Wilson in 1918 it was estimated that the number of these spiral nebulae visible in the heavens must be of the order of half a million at least. (For a particularly fine example, *see* Plate I.)

Despite their peculiar structure and enormous numbers, these nebulae too were thought to be constituent members of the Galaxy. However, as a result of observations made with the Mount Wilson telescope opinion rapidly changed. The decisive criterion was found by Hubble in 1924 when he succeeded in identifying Cepheid variables in the nearer spirals. He thereby concluded that the distances of these objects is of the order of a million light-years or about five times that of the globular star clusters. Hence the spirals lay definitely outside the Galaxy, and our conception of the depth of the universe was correspondingly magnified.

The history of cosmology is a history of receding backgrounds. After Hubble's capital discovery, it was at last clear that the Galaxy is not the ultimate background of the universe. Beyond lie other systems, and it is now believed that with the largest telescopes many millions of external or extragalactic nebulae can be seen. The estimation of their distances was the first step in the study of the structure of this super-system of the heavens.

Cepheid variables can be identified only in a comparatively small number of the nebulae, but by estimating their distances Hubble deduced in 1929 that the brightest constituent stars of these nebulae were all of about the same absolute luminosity, averaging about 50,000 times that of the Sun. Thus, these stars provided a second criterion (Hubble's *brightest star criterion*) for estimating the distances of those nebulae, about 150 in number, in which individual stars could be detected. Furthermore, this selection of nebulae was used by Hubble to provide a third statistical criterion of distance applicable when other methods fail. Most of these nebulae were found to have luminosities falling within a range of one-half to twice the average, which is about 1,700 times brighter than that of their brightest stars. The distribution of absolute magnitude is therefore much more concentrated for nebulae than for stars; hence, while Herschel's assumption that the first magnitude stars are at one distance, the second magnitude at another and so on, has long been abandoned, a similar principle continued to be employed in studying the distribution of the nebulae. The criterion was essentially statistical; although individual results were considered to be uncertain, mean results for large numbers of nebulae were thought to be fairly reliable.

This method of successive calibration was used by Hubble to the very limits of the 100-inch telescope. In his opinion, the weakest link in the chain was the second, the brightest star criterion; for he could not be sure that the collection of nebulae to which it applied constituted a fair sample. However, with its aid Hubble was able to draw up an awe-inspiring distance scale for the universe, which completely dwarfed all previous scientifically based conceptions of its extent.

Having finally decided that the vast majority of nebulae lie outside the Galactic system, the next step was to determine their approximate size. At first it was thought that once the distances of the nearer nebulae, such as the great nebula in Andromeda, had been estimated to within a probable error of about ten per cent., it would be a comparatively simple matter to calculate their dimensions from the images recorded on photographic plates. However, it soon appeared that, according to this crude method, every one of these nebulae must be several times smaller than the Galaxy. Later it was realized that attention had been concentrated on those regions in which stars were sufficiently numerous to affect the photographic plates to an extent visible to the unaided eye, and when the plates were studied with the aid of special instruments it was found that the nebulae were far more extensive than had previously been thought. Meanwhile evidence continued to accumulate that the spiral nebulae were broadly similar structures to the Milky Way. In particular, in 1932 Hubble discovered that the Andromeda nebula was accompanied by over one hundred objects which from their form and structure he concluded to be globular clusters similar to those surrounding our Galaxy. These clusters extended well beyond the ordinary photographic limits and about doubled the apparent diameter of the nebula. Other evidence concerning its detailed contents led to a growing conviction that this nebula in particular possessed a markedly similar structure to our own stellar system.

Moreover, just as there was increasing evidence that earlier estimates of the size of the Andromeda nebula were too small, so with increasing knowledge concerning interstellar light-absorbing material it was realized that Shapley's original estimate of the size of the Galaxy was too large, the apparent faintness of its more distant parts being increased by the additional amount of interstellar fog to be penetrated before their light could reach the Earth. (On the other hand, the intervening space between our Galaxy and external systems was thought to be comparatively transparent and free of diffuse matter.) Nevertheless, many astronomers continued to be puzzled by the fact that, although the Andromeda nebula was so similar, our Galaxy appeared to be larger than any other stellar system.

When the Andromeda nebula was compared with other nebulae outside the Galaxy, a new complication was encountered—the question of shape. The form of our own Galaxy is not easy for us to assess owing to our internal position, but it has long been known that many of the nebulae which are now regarded as lying outside the Galaxy do not exhibit the characteristic spiral shape. Of course, this can often be attributed to their faintness, only the central portions showing up on the photographic plate; indeed, in the great majority of cases the plates reveal mere formless specks similar to the images of faint stars. The first systematic study of the shape of a group of nebulae which are all at about the same distance from us was made by Hubble in 1926. Any difference in apparent shape in such a group must be due to a difference in real shape. Hubble examined a cluster of 167 nebulae in Virgo and discovered that only about one in two were of spiral form.

Other investigations since have tended to confirm that many nebulae are definitely not spiral, but are either elliptical or else highly irregular. However, owing both to their distance and to the fact that in nearly every cluster of nebulae both forms occur, it is clear that we are justified in placing all these systems in the same category. Hence, we call all these objects collectively the *extragalactic nebulae*,[1] to distinguish them from the much

[1] The term *galaxies* has also been employed, particularly in recent years.

smaller gaseous type which is found to lie inside the Galaxy.

Another criterion which confirms this classification is that of spectral type. It is well known that light is radiated in waves of different lengths. In general, light from a given source is composite, and with the aid of a glass prism or grating can be decomposed into different colours, each colour corresponding to a definite wavelength, the deflections by the prism being least for the long red waves and greatest for the short violet waves. The whole rainbow sequence is called a *spectrum*, and each definite colour or relative position in the spectrum corresponds to definite wave-length. The relative brightness of any colour indicates the relative abundance of radiation of the corresponding wave-length. Different types of radiating bodies give rise to characteristic spectra. Thus an incandescent solid or dense gas yields a continuous spectrum; on the other hand, an incandescent gas at low pressure radiates only isolated colours, so that its spectrum, known as an *emission spectrum*, consists of bright lines and dark gaps. As each gas has a spectrum of a characteristic pattern, it is possible to identify the constituent gases in a distant light source by spectrum analysis.

A star such as the Sun presents a third type of spectrum. The main body of the Sun provides a continuous spectrum; but the surrounding solar atmosphere, although gaseous, does not furnish an emission spectrum because it is at a lower temperature. Instead, the gas absorbs from the continuous background the colours which it would normally emit. Consequently, the solar spectrum has a continuous background on which is superimposed a pattern of dark lines which are due to gaps in the continuous background. This is known as an *absorption spectrum*. Certain nebulae exhibit emission spectra and hence must be gaseous. These nebulae have all been found to lie within our own Galaxy. On the other hand, the extragalactic nebulae exhibit absorption spectra characteristic of starlight and so are probably composed of stars, and possibly of dark matter too.

The Sun's spectrum is dominated by the lines of hydrogen and certain metallic vapours, in particular a pair of lines in the violet region due to calcium, known as the H and K lines. It happens that the spectra of the extragalactic nebulae are very similar to the solar spectrum, indicating that a high proportion of the light from these stellar systems must be due to stars of the same type as the Sun. It is a most fortunate circumstance that, although the light from the nebulae is so faint that it can be spread only over very short spectra, it is possible to identify some of their lines and, in particular, the H and K lines of calcium.

Spectrum analysis was first applied successfully to the Sun about 1814 by Fraunhofer who established conclusively that the Sun produces an absorption spectrum; the characteristic dark lines in the solar spectrum are known as Fraunhofer's lines. Forty years, however, elapsed before the general principles of spectroscopy were laid down by Kirchhoff. Nevertheless, as early as 1842 one of the key principles was enunciated by an Austrian mathematician, Christian Doppler; it is of outstanding importance in its application to the stars and nebulae. It is well known that the whistle of an engine is shriller when approaching than when receding. This is due to the fact that in the former case the sound waves are more compressed. Similarly, Doppler argued that the light waves from an approaching source are also compressed and those from a receding source correspondingly elongated, the degree of compression or elongation depending on the speed. A general shortening of wave-length would mean that the spectrum would be shifted bodily towards the violet, while a lengthening would shift it towards the red, the fractional displacement (ratio of shift to original wave-length) in each case being equal to the ratio of the speed of the source to the speed of light. This is known as the *Doppler effect*. It is usually very small.

Nevertheless, the great British pioneer of astronomical spectroscopy, Sir William Huggins, realized that Doppler's principle could be used to determine the radial velocity of celestial bodies; that is, their velocity in the line of sight. 'It would scarcely be possible,' said Huggins, 'to convey any true conception of the difficulties which presented themselves in this work from various instrumental causes and of the extreme care and caution which were needed to distinguish spurious instrumental shifts of a line from a true shift due to a star's motion.'

However, Huggins overcame all difficulties and obtained the first crude measurements; he announced in 1868 that Sirius was receding from the solar system at twenty-nine miles per second, the correct order of magnitude. He also measured the radial velocities of other well-known stars.

Huggins' pioneer work was purely visual. The full flowering of spectroscopic astronomy came only with the application of photography at the end of the nineteenth century. Hence, exploration of the very difficult field of nebular spectra was not begun until the second decade of the twentieth century. Thus it happened that the most striking feature of the extragalactic nebulae was not discovered until about forty years ago, as a result of the momentous pioneer research of Dr. V. M. Slipher of the Lowell Observatory. In 1912 Slipher first obtained the spectrum of the great nebula in Andromeda and announced that it was moving towards the solar system at the rate of 125 miles per second. By 1917 he had photographed the spectra of fifteen spirals, all but two of which he found receding with velocities averaging about twenty-five times the average velocity of the stars, or about 400 miles per second. Although these velocities were enormous, the standard procedure of attributing the observed spectral shifts to the Doppler effect was not immediately called in question. Indeed, no other interpretation appeared to be acceptable. Whatever the ultimate explanation may prove to be, the fact that the spectra of these nebulae are shifted bodily towards the red is indisputable. This extraordinary phenomenon was of crucial significance for the classification of the nebulae, for the gaseous type exhibited no pronounced systematic spectral shift.

The velocities attributed by Slipher to the nearer spirals, although enormous compared with stellar velocities, did not exceed one per cent. of the velocity of light. However, the fact that the vast majority of these nebulae appeared to be receding from our neighbourhood was difficult to reconcile with the idea that their motions were purely random. It was therefore necessary to determine whether this phenomenon applied to more distant nebulae. Unfortunately, most of these are so faint that adequate spectrograms could only be obtained with the aid of the 100-inch reflector at Mount Wilson, and exposures lasting several nights were essential.[1]

In 1929 Humason began to photograph the spectra of increa-

---

[1] This was a tremendously difficult undertaking. First one point of light among thousands of others all around it had to be kept steadily fixed over the slit of a spectograph attached to the telescope for, perhaps, eight or ten

singly fainter nebulae with this great telescope. Within a few years he had amassed an amazing series of photographs indicating a progressive reddening of spectra with increasing faintness and hence with increasing distance. At the limits of observation with his instruments Humason recorded red-shifts corresponding to velocities of recession of nearly 25,000 miles per second or about one-seventh of the velocity of light. As Hubble has reminded us, such velocities are equivalent to circumnavigating the Earth in a second or travelling to the Moon in ten seconds. Moreover, red-shifts appeared to increase still further beyond the limit of the spectrograph.

Thus the existence of a systematic red-shift increasing with increasing faintness was definitely established. The law correlating shift with distance was first predicted theoretically; it was not until 1929, when Hubble had devised his brightest star criterion of distance, that a sufficient quantity of data could be assembled to confirm the linear relation between distance and shift now known as *Hubble's law*. If one nebula is twice as far as another, then its spectrum will be shifted to the red twice as far relatively, and so on.

At first this law was known to be valid only out to distances of about 6 million light-years, but by 1931 it had been extended to a distance of the order of 150 million light-years. Further extension of the law was difficult, because of the uncertainties in estimating the distances of the fainter nebulae. In particular, correcting factors in the calculation of distance from apparent brightness will vary according to the interpretation of the red-shift phenomenon. For a nebula receding with a high velocity will appear fainter than a similar nebula which is at rest relative to us: recession will thin out the incoming stream of radiation and hence reduce the apparent brightness by an amount proportional to the red-shift. However, if the systematic red-shifts were interpreted as Doppler shifts, then it appeared that the nearer extragalactic nebulae, at least, were receding from us in all directions with velocities proportional to their observed distances. The rate of increase of velocity with distance was

nights. Then, after all this concentrated effort, the resulting picture might be no more than one-tenth of an inch long and one-thirtieth of an inch wide containing many closely packed lines! With modern equipment, including not only the 200-inch telescope but also diffraction gratings, faster cameras and sensitive photographic plates, it is now possible to obtain such spectra in less than an hour.

thought to be about 540 kilometres per second per megaparsec, or roughly 100 miles per second per million light-years. (*See* Plate III.)

On this interpretation the evidence pointed to an extraordinary and unique state of affairs. *Assuming that the radial velocities have remained sensibly constant*, it was calculated that about 1,800 million years ago the nebulae were all clustered together; and since then they have all been rushing away in all possible directions with all possible speeds. As it seemed in the highest degree unlikely that our own Galaxy is a peculiar centre of repulsion, astronomers were driven to the conclusion that, on this view, the whole system of nebulae was expanding.

Whatever the ultimate verdict on this conclusion, it was clear that the system of nebulae is markedly different from the Galaxy. Moreover, unlike the Galaxy, this system showed no sign of petering out at great distances. In each direction increasing numbers of nebulae were visible right up to the very threshold of observation. It seemed that we had at last encountered the ultimate background of the universe—the system of extragalactic nebulae, extending to the horizon of space accessible to our instruments. Accepting the view that this system is in process of expansion, we were immediately confronted with the possibility that the universe had existed in its present state only for a period of the order of 2,000 million years.

It is not surprising that this picture of the world did not meet with universal acceptance. Attempts were repeatedly made to find other possible explanations of the red-shift phenomenon. For example, Zwicky suggested that light automatically loses energy in traversing the gravitational fields of matter distributed between us and the nebulae, but his calculations have not been generally accepted. To most astronomers there seemed to be but two alternative solutions to the problem. These were well summarized by Hubble as follows: 'Red-shifts are produced either in the nebulae, where the light originates, or in the intervening space through which the light travels. If the source is in the nebulae, then red-shifts are probably velocity-shifts and the nebulae are receding. If the source lies in the intervening space, the explanation of red-shifts is unknown, but the nebulae are sensibly stationary.'[1]

[1] A different possible solution (Milne's τ-theory) is discussed in Chapter 6.

Unfortunately, the crucial test for deciding between these two possibilities appeared to result in a vicious circle. For, as already mentioned, a receding nebula should appear fainter than a stationary nebula of the same intrinsic luminosity at the same distance. Hence, it was suggested that, if the distance of a nebula were known, its apparent faintness could be used as a criterion of motion. However, as Hubble pointed out, the only information concerning great distances was derived from the same apparent luminosities which he wished to test. Actually the situation was even more complex than portrayed by Hubble, for he assumed that the average absolute luminosity of the more distant nebulae is the same as that of the nearer. Although the range in intrinsic brightness of the nearer nebulae[1] is less than that of the stars, it is not a necessary consequence of the principle of the uniformity of nature that the average instrinsic brightness of the more distant nebulae must be the same as that of the nearer. The light received from the former gives us information about the state of these nebulae hundreds of millions of years ago, and it is possible that the luminosity of any given nebula varies appreciably during such vast intervals of time.

We thus see that the distance and motion of the nebulae cannot be measured directly without hypothesis. Indeed, the whole problem bristles with complications. By combining observation and hypothesis various world-models have been constructed and preference for any one of these depends on theoretical considerations. Consequently, there still is far less agreement about the properties of the system of nebulae than about those of the Galaxy.

There is, however, one outstanding feature of the system of nebulae on which there is fairly general agreement. It arises from counts of nebulae to various limits of faintness. These counts were made in two different ways. At the Mount Wilson and Lick Observatories, large telescopes were used to study small areas systematically scattered over the northern sky. Meanwhile, at the Harvard College Observatory and at its southern station, large areas of the sky were studied with the aid of moderate-sized telescopes.

Counts of nebulae to various limits of apparent faintness made in these two different ways *at first* appeared to yield discordant

[1] It is of the order of 1,000 to 1.

results. In 1938 Shapley, who was responsible for the Harvard programme, argued that there was pronounced evidence of a general
density-gradient; he maintained that, as our telescopes sweep across
the sky, they find more nebulae in one region than in another. On
the other hand, Hubble and his co-workers, who were responsible
for the Mount Wilson programme, claimed that in the three-quarters
of the sky accessible to their telescopes there was no evidence of any
real density-gradient, although there was an apparent gradient, the
nebulae appearing to avoid the zone of the Milky Way and to
congregate most thickly towards the galactic poles.

Statistical analysis of this apparent gradient showed that, if a
correcting factor was introduced to compensate for the light-
absorbing effect of the interstellar 'fog' which is spread throughout
our Galaxy, then the corrected distribution was effectively uniform
in each direction. However, as statistical analysis is valid only if
larger number of objects are studied, it was necessary to include
many faint nebulae. Hubble showed that the mean results of the
two methods were substantially the same, indicating that the overall
distribution of the extragalactic nebulae is in fact *isotropic*, that is
effectively identical in each direction, so that we are at a centre of
symmetry. Despite past controversies, we can regard this result as
one of the more reliable features of our knowledge of these distant
systems.

The fact that we appear to be centrally situated in the field of the
nebulae is of vital theoretical significance. Let us compare our
apparent position relative to the system of galaxies with our apparent
position in our own Galaxy. Prior to Shapley's work on the distribution of globular clusters the Sun was thought to be situated at the
centre of our Galaxy, but this was ultimately seen to be a wrong
conclusion arising from inadequate knowledge. The Milky Way
does not extend in the same fashion in all directions, but is bun-
shaped and has an ultimate boundary. Consequently, only a comparatively small percentage of stars can be situated at or near the
centre of this system. It is improbable that our Sun should happen
to be one of these, and in fact we now realize that our Sun is not
central.

On the other hand, the system of nebulae appears to be spherically symmetrically distributed around us and to have no visible

boundary. It is theoretically possible, as we shall see, for an un-bounded distribution of matter to have its circumference nowhere and centre everywhere. Thus the apparent spherical symmetry of the system of nebulae and the absence of a visible boundary can be reconciled with our aversion to pre-Copernican anthropocentric con-ceptions of the universe, provided that the system of nebulae has a multitude of centres. If this is so, it is clear that the system must be unbounded, for a nebula on the boundary could not be centrally situated. But if the system of nebulae is unbounded it must form the ultimate background of the physical universe. We have already referred to this possibility, but the present argument puts it in its proper perspective. Although the evidence is not wholly conclusive, in the present state of our knowledge this assumption forms the basis of almost all cosmological theories.

When we pass from the consideration of the symmetry to the problem of the distribution in depth of the system of the nebulae, we encounter peculiar difficulties. As we have seen, there is no sign of any 'thinning out' of the system as we penetrate into the remotest depths accessible to the largest telescopes, but strictly speaking this statement needs some qualification. It is true that so far there is no sign of the system 'petering out' at the limits of our vision, but the problem of deciding whether there is any actual 'thinning out' at great distances is extremely complex.

The observational data enable us to draw up a table of the total numbers of nebulae, seen in a particular square degree of the sky, brighter than certain limiting magnitudes, e.g. 18th magnitude, 19th magnitude and so on. These magnitudes represent different degrees of apparent brightness, and the crux of the problem concerns the precise significance which we must attach to this concept. For the apparent brightness of an extragalactic nebula (corrected for all 'local' effects such as the dimming due to interstellar light-absorb-ing material in the Milky Way) depends not only on its intrinsic brightness when it emitted the light which we now receive but also on its red-shift, and the effect of this is greater for the more remote, and therefore fainter, nebulae. According to current ideas, this shift, whatever its cause, diminishes the energy of the light emitted and so makes the nebula appear to be fainter than it would otherwise. But this is not the only complication which becomes progressively more serious for the remoter nebulae. This true absolute magnitude of a star or nebula (known as its *bolometric magnitude*) depends on the total radiation of all wave-lengths which it emits, whereas the observed apparent magnitude on the photographic plate is confined to certain parts of the spectrum. The red-shift of the spectrum therefore introduces a peculiar complication, known as the K-term, into the problem of converting from photographically determined apparent magnitudes to bolometric magnitudes.

In interpreting the observational data as evidence for the distribution of nebulae in depth, Hubble examined alternative hypotheses concerning the cause of the red-shift, but he assumed throughout that the average absolute luminosity of the more distant nebulae is the same as that of those nearby and that the geometry of the intervening space is effectively Euclidean, so that in consequence apparent brightness diminishes as the square of the distance.

As a result of his investigations, Hubble was inclined, from about 1936, to reject the Doppler-effect interpretation of the red shifts and to regard the nebulae as stationary; but theoretical cosmologists, notably McVittie in the late nineteen-thirties and Heckmann in the early nineteen-forties, severely criticized Hubble's method of analysing the observational results and disputed his conclusions. Although these criticisms of Hubble's analysis came to be generally accepted, it still seemed that the available data were open to rival interpretations, depending on the method of analysis adopted.

Meanwhile it was generally hoped by astronomers that the construction of still larger telescopes would help to elucidate the intriguing data revealed by the 100-inch reflector. At last, in 1949, the great 200-inch Hale telescope on Mount Palomar was ready for use, and new observational results were eagerly awaited. The first significant step forward was made by Humason who succeeded in photographing the spectra of two remote galaxies in the Hydra cluster. These exhibited red-shifts which, on the Doppler interpretation, indicated velocities of recession of about 38,000 miles per second or one-fifth of the velocity of light.[1] Several years later, in 1956, with the aid of special photoelectric equipment attached to the new telescope, Baum obtained a red-shift corresponding to a recessional velocity of about two-fifths of the velocity of light. (If it were

[1] *See* Plate III.

possible to travel in an aeroplane at such a speed we could circumnavigate the Earth's equator three times in a second!)

Although these achievements were spectacular, the results obtained were not surprising. The most important consequence, however, of the introduction of the new telescope was utterly unexpected by the vast majority of astronomers and theoretical cosmologists. At the meeting of the International Astronomical Union in Rome in September, 1952, Baade, one of the most distinguished observers on Mount Palomar, announced that Hubble's entire distance scale was in error, not only at the uncertain far end but even at the near end where it was previously believed to be accurate to within about ten per cent. According to Baade, the distances formerly assigned to all extragalactic objects must be multiplied by a factor of about *two*. Later it was generally accepted that this scale-factor was probably nearer *three*. Since the spatial dimensions attributed to any external nebula are calculated by multiplying its angular extension in the sky by its distance, it followed that the sizes of all such objects had been underestimated. In particular, the Andromeda nebula is now recognized to be significantly larger than the Milky Way, although its general structure is still thought to be basically similar.

Indeed, it was his belief in the close similarity between this nebula and our own stellar system that had convinced Baade that Hubble's extragalactic distance-scale must be in error. For example, observers had been led to expect that the 200-inch reflector ought to be able to resolve the globular clusters surrounding the Andromeda nebula so that their brightest constituent stars could be easily detected. This telescope can photograph objects down to an apparent magnitude of 22·5. If the Andromeda nebula were at the distance estimated by Hubble, about 750,000 light-years, then the Cepheid-type variables of short period (less than a day) which abound in its globular clusters and central regions (as in those of the Milky Way) should be of apparent magnitude 21·8. Consequently, many of these stars (known as RR Lyrae variables[1]), which are believed to be all very nearly of the same absolute magnitude, should have been readily detected. None were found on the photographs, however,

[1] To distinguish them from the so-called classical Cepheids which have periods of ten days or more.

and even with exposures lasting thirty minutes there appeared in the regions where they were sought only stars which were known to be about one and a half magnitudes more luminous. Therefore, it looked as if the distance-scale for the Andromeda nebula was wrong by a factor of about two, corresponding to a difference on the magnitude-scale of about one and a half, and that this nebula must be roughly twice as far away as had previously been supposed.

There were other reasons for coming to the same conclusion. The globular clusters surrounding the Andromeda nebula appeared to be systematically smaller than those surrounding the Milky Way, being on the average of about half the diameter. This discrepancy would disappear if they were about twice as far away as previously supposed. Another discrepancy which the suggested change in extra-galactic distances would resolve concerned the average absolute magnitude at maximum brightness of novae (stars which suddenly and temporarily increase about a hundred-thousandfold or more in brightness). These occur at the rate of twenty or more a year in both systems, but those in the Milky Way attain on the average a maximum absolute magnitude of about −7·4, whereas those observed in the Andromeda appeared to attain only about −5·7. Here the discrepancy was a little more than one and a half, and the apparent anomaly could be removed by placing the Andromeda nebula rather more than twice as far away as previously. It is now thought to be at a distance of some one and three quarter million light-years, but Baade's definitive paper on this problem has not yet been published.

The reason why all extragalactic distances had previously been underestimated is because of an error in converting the scale of relative distances of Cepheid variables into an absolute scale. It will be remembered that an estimate of the distance of at least one Cepheid, made independently of the period-luminosity law, was required to fix the absolute scale, and evidently a mistake had been made. This mistake did not apply, however, to the distances assigned to the RR Lyrae variables, but only to the Cepheids of longer periods. As the former predominate in globular clusters, forming more than ninety per cent. of the variables found in them, they had served as the basis for determining the size of the Milky Way. Consequently, the dimensions of our own stellar system were completely unaffected by Baade's revision of the distance-scale which, therefore, applied only to extragalactic objects. Independent investigations of RR Lyrae stars in the Magellanic Clouds and, to a lesser extent, the new determination of the statistical parallaxes of a group of classical Cepheids in our own Galaxy, confirmed Baade's correction. Although the absolute distance-scale of the classical Cepheids is still far from being precisely determined, it is now generally accepted that Hubble's distance-scale for the universe must be revised in accordance with Baade's suggestion.

Baade's revision of extragalactic distances had momentous consequences concerning the size and the age of the universe, for the scale of both was correspondingly increased. The most remote nebulae observed with the Mount Palomar telescope were now estimated to be 2,000 million light-years away. At this distance there was still no sign of a boundary. It is an awe-inspiring thought that the light-waves from the most distant objects which now blur our photographic plates were already at least three parts of the way to us when the oldest known fossils in terrestrial rocks were first being formed. Although the distances formerly assigned to the nebulae must be increased, the velocities attributed to them were unaffected because they were deduced directly from the observed spectral shifts and these were not changed by the revision of the distance-scale. Assuming that the red-shifts were due to recessional motion, the rate of increase of velocity with distance was calculated to be about 180 kilometres per second per megaparsec. If the velocities have remained sensibly uniform throughout the past, then according to Baade, the age of the universe would be between five and six thousand million years.

An important new survey of the law relating red-shifts and magnitudes published in 1956 by Humason, Mayall and Sandage suggested, however, that the expansion of the universe may have been faster in the past than now so that its age may be somewhat less than that estimated on the hypothesis of uniform expansion. But this conclusion must be regarded with great caution, for a recent review (1958) by Sandage of Hubble's criteria for constructing the extragalactic distance-scale has revealed that, not only must his Cepheid criterion be corrected, but also the *second* link in his chain —the brightest star criterion; the precise correction is not yet known.

With regard to the former, Baade's discovery that the classical Cepheids were about 1·5 magnitudes brighter than had been thought is not the only correction required. Since then it has been found that individual Cepheids of the same period do *not* all have *precisely* the same absolute luminosity. The spread may be as much as 1·2 magnitudes for a given period, and this, as Sandage points out, introduces a new factor into our use of these stars as reliable distance-indicators. For the astronomer must decide whether a particular Cepheid is 'over-luminous' or 'under-luminous' for its period. No doubt, reliable methods for making such decisions will eventually be evolved as the result of more intensive study of Cepheids, e.g. in the Magellanic Clouds.

As for Hubble's brightest star criterion, Sandage himself has shown that objects in the Virgo cluster of galaxies which Hubble believed to be highly luminous stars are in fact regions of glowing hydrogen of intrinsic luminosity about two magnitudes brighter than that assumed by Hubble. If Sandage's result is accepted, then the distances of all galaxies beyond those in which Cepheids can be detected with our most powerful telescopes must be augmented by a factor of between 5 and 10, as compared with Hubble's old values, with the result that the rate of increase of velocity with distance will be reduced to between 50 and 100 kilometres per second per megaparsec. Consequently, taking 80 as a rough average value, the age of the universe, if it has expanded uniformly, will have to be increased to about 13·5 thousand million years. If, however, we accept the view that it was expanding more rapidly in the past than now, this figure might be reduced to about 9 thousand million years.

Yet another correction to Hubble's figure for the rate of increase of velocity with distance was advocated in November, 1958, by de Vaucouleurs. He claims that the Milky Way is a member of a vast super-cluster of galaxies with its centre near the Virgo cluster. Departures from the strictly linear velocity-distance law for clusters in this putative super-cluster are interpreted by him as due to rotation about the centre, so that the super-cluster as a whole is both expanding and rotating. If de Vaucouleurs' contention is basically correct, the value formerly assigned to the relative velocity of recession of the Virgo cluster (the principal datum enabling us to determine the rate of recession of the nebulae per megaparsec) will have to be corrected for the effect of rotation about the super-cluster centre. He believes that the Sandage value may have to be increased to a figure nearer 150 kilometres per second per megaparsec. In this case, the age of the universe, if we assume it to be expanding uniformly, may lie between 7 and 10 thousand million years. If, however, it expanded more rapidly in the past than now, its present age might be about 6 thousand million years.

These successive major changes in cosmical distances and times provide us with a salutary reminder that pure observations tell us very little until they receive theoretical interpretation. Indeed, many modern ideas concerning the universe, notably those originating in the Copernican revolution, began not with new facts but from looking at old facts in a new way. This does not mean that we should underestimate the value of the data so laboriously collected by observational astronomers over many centuries. On them Copernicus based his theory, but new theoretical concepts and hypotheses were required to give it the shape and pattern with which we are now familiar.

Copernicus was concerned with the solar system, the foreground of the universe. Today we believe we have encountered the ultimate background of the universe, the system of extragalactic nebulae. Again we are presented with a complicated tangle of observations and hypotheses. Further observations may assist us in resolving many current controversies, but a clear understanding of the problem will always depend as much on fruitful theoretical concepts, freely constructed by the intellect, as on 'stubborn and irreducible' factual data.

3

SPACE AND TIME

SO FAR we have considered some of the principal results of recent exploration of the universe with the telescope and spectroscope. In assembling the observational evidence we have found that the picture which emerges depends on our method of interpretation. There are two conflicting points of view concerning the general nature of scientific method, which we will consider in turn.

In the early seventeenth century Francis Bacon maintained that natural science consisted solely in the patient accumulation of facts. Later in the same century Isaac Newton defined his method of scientific investigation in the famous epigram, *Hypotheses non fingo*.[1] The extraordinary success of modern natural science, the foundations of which were laid in the seventeenth century, has caused widespread acceptance of this empirical fundamentalism. The ultimate court of appeal is said to be the data of observation, which are considered as absolute and independent of the human mind. In the nineteenth century this positivistic point of view was almost universal among men of science. The reaction against it has set in only since the scope of scientific investigation has been so vastly extended on the scale of the very large and of the very small that the classical methods of interpreting phenomena have been found inadequate.

The alternative point of view is that science begins with questioning. It was first enunciated by Kant towards the end of the

[1] 'I make no hypotheses.' In fact Newton was a great user and inventor of hypotheses. His famous statement is usually quoted without reference to its context: the problem of the nature, or mechanism, of gravitation. The success of Newton's theory was, however, due to his side-stepping of this baffling question, producing instead an extraordinarily powerful technique for describing and calculating gravitational motions.

eighteenth century. In a famous passage in the preface to the second edition of *The Critique of Pure Reason* he wrote:

'When Galileo caused balls, the weights of which he had himself previously determined, to roll down an inclined plane, when Torricelli made the air carry a weight which he had calculated beforehand to be equal to that of a definite column of water; or in more recent times, when Stahl changed metal into lime, and lime back again into metal, by withdrawing something and then restoring it, a light broke upon all students of nature. They learned that reason has insight only into that which it produces after a plan of its own, and that it must not allow itself to be kept, as it were, in nature's leading-strings, but must itself show the way with principles of judgment based upon fixed laws, constraining nature to give answer to questions of reason's own determining. Accidental observations, made in obedience to no previously thought-out plan, can never be made to yield a necessary law, which alone reason is concerned to discover. Reason, holding in one hand its principles, according to which alone concordant appearances can be admitted as equivalent to laws, and in the other hand the experiment which it has devised in conformity with these principles, must approach nature in order to be taught by it. It must not, however, do so in the character of a pupil who listens to everything that the teacher chooses to say, but of an appointed judge who compels the witnesses to answer questions which he himself has formulated. Even physics, therefore, owes the beneficent revolution in its point of view entirely to the happy thought, that while reason must seek in nature, not fictitiously ascribe to it, whatever as not being knowable through reason's own resources has to be learnt, if learnt at all, only from nature, it must adopt as its guide, in so seeking, that which it has itself put into nature. It is thus that the study of nature has entered on the secure path of a science, after having for so many centuries been nothing but a process of merely random groping.'

Kant himself believed that there were unique answers to all fundamental scientific questions, because he maintained that these questions did not concern things-in-themselves (which he regarded as essentially 'unknowable') but the conceptions of things which the human mind was compelled by its own nature to formulate, and these he thought were unique. Kant's theory of science has been accepted by few modern scientists, although some, notably Poincaré and Eddington, have developed their own views on the basis of it. Instead of Kant's historically important but out-dated theory, a more realistic view is that fundamental scientific problems do not automatically possess unique solutions, since these depend on our initial choice of assumptions and hypotheses. *A science completely devoid of presuppositions is impossible.* In many investigations, however, long experience has taught us which are the most convenient hypotheses to adopt for the purpose in hand, and we feel no need to question this choice. Yet in other investigations it is found sooner or later that one basic assumption or another must be questioned if progress is to be made.

This situation confronts us when we try to interpret recent observations of the extragalactic nebulae. Controversies have arisen not only because of the inadequacy of the observational data, but also because the nebulae are assumed to constitute the ultimate background of the physical universe concerning which no general agreement has yet been reached. Assumptions about this background are implicit in all branches of physical science, but generally these branches are not very sensitive to the actual assumptions adopted. When, however, we come to consider the background itself, then these assumptions are necessarily of crucial significance. A satisfactory theory of the structure of the universe must, therefore, depend on an adequate analysis of these presuppositions, in particular the ideas of space and time.

The origin of these ideas is lost in the mists of prehistory. The study of contemporary primitive races, however, suggests that the earliest ideas were probably rather complicated. It seems that for primitive people time consisted of disconnected fragments; there was no concept of time as a whole, only of convenient fractions of time, e.g. so many moons. The earliest civilization arose as a result of the invention of agriculture, which must have focused attention on periodical phenomena in nature; indeed, the oldest civilizations are remarkable for their highly elaborate calendars. Nevertheless, the methods of measuring short intervals of time were extremely crude. It will be recalled that as late as the end of the sixteenth century Galileo used his pulse-beat to discover the regularity of the swinging pendulum.[1] In the earliest methods of time reckoning, there were no hours or shorter intervals. Also there was no precise idea of an instant; for example, the shortest interval of time indicated by the Egyptians was depicted in hieroglyphics simply by the upraised head of a hippopotamus with a line cutting it, presumably signifying the period during which the animal thrust its head out of the water for a quick look round. The idea of an hour was developed as a definite fraction of the period of daylight and varied in length according to the season; the hour of fixed length was introduced only with the advent of the striking clock in the fourteenth century.

Similarly, the earliest ideas of space were also extremely complex. In addition to the all-important distinction between up and down, there appeared to be little similarity between one direction and another. We believe that Geometry, or the science of space, was developed originally by the Egyptians and others for the purposes of surveying. Its subsequent transformation by the Greeks into a general abstract discipline, based on axioms and definitions, was one of the most remarkable revolutions in the history of thought. This free creation of the intellect depended on a drastic simplification of the concept of space, thereby artificially attributing to it ideas of homogeneity and immutability. There appears, however, to have been a significant difference between the space of the Greek geo-meters and the space of the Greek philosophers of Nature. The latter was more in accord with primitive ideas. It was dominated by the idea of 'place': every natural object has its natural position in the universe, towards which it tends to move unless constrained. Thus in natural space there was absolute position and absolute motion.

The idea of the universe as a whole appears to have been another original creation of the Greek intellect. The Babylonians believed in an 'inevitable necessity' dominating all things, but they do not seem to have had any clear idea of the unity of the universe. As far as we know, the first cosmologist was Thales of Miletus who lived in the sixth century B.C. He maintained that 'everything is water'. Thus, the idea of the unity of the universe was first expressed in terms of an underlying invariant substance. This tendency to abstract some-thing fixed from the eternal flux of phenomena persisted in ancient

[1] Even if the story about the swinging lamp in Pisa Cathedral is untrue, he certainly had no timekeeper more accurate than his pulse.

thought and ultimately resulted in the construction of geometrical models of the universe, in which every object had its allotted position, the whole system being eternal.

The idea of time played a comparatively minor role in Greek thought. It was not refined and developed to the same extent as the idea of space. This comparative neglect of time has had a tremendous subsequent influence and has been responsible for the basically geometrical character of most systems of natural philosophy. The reasons for this neglect were manifold; in particular, it appeared that time was not easily amenable to logical analysis. For example, Zeno claimed to show by a set of ingenious paradoxes that the ideas of time and motion were self-contradictory. In fact, these paradoxes do not disprove the existence of motion, but instead expose certain difficulties associated with the abstract concept of an instant of time. For example, in the paradox of the arrow, Zeno argued that it is at rest during its flight since at each instant it occupies a space equal to itself; but what always occupies a space equal to itself is not in motion and is therefore at rest.

Zeno devised his paradoxes with the object of confuting the followers of Pythagoras. Pythagoras and his school maintained that the ultimate realities in nature were numbers. This doctrine was put forward by Pythagoras after the discovery of the numerical ratio between the length of a string and the pitch of its note. The Pythagoreans were extremely interested in the periodicity of the universe, and one of them, Archytas of Tarentum who was a contemporary of Plato, is noteworthy for his definition of time: 'Time is the number of a certain movement and in its widest sense the interval of the natural order of the universe.' Space was regarded by the Pythagoreans as an assemblage of points, although points were considered to be of finite size and not dimensionless. Every object was thought to be composed of a certain number of points arranged in a definite order.

By exposing the logical difficulties inherent in the Pythagorean ideas, Zeno gave strong support to the rival theory of Parmenides who maintained that the world was a continuous indivisible sphere always identical with itself. Despite the obvious incompatibility of this concept with our most elementary sense data, this theory has had a profound influence on the development of human thought, causing attention to be directed to those features of the world which are independent of the flow of time, and emphasizing the unity of the universe.

For the Greeks time appears to have been primarily an objective phenomenon characterizing the appearance of the external world. Questions concerning subjective or psychological time were first raised by St. Augustine whose famous query, '*Quid est tempus? Si nemo a me quaerat, scio, si quaerenti explicare velim, nescio !*'[1] signified that he was unable to construct a theory of his intuition of time and could not relate it to the objective time-order created by God. The problem concerned him profoundly. 'My soul is on fire,' he cried, 'to know this most intricate enigma.'

During the Middle Ages time was regarded teleologically. Instead of picturing it as flowing from past to future, mediaeval philosophers depicted it as the flow of the future (potentiality) into the present (actuality). The theory was essentially qualitative, although in the fourteenth century the first preliminary attempts were made to develop a mathematical analysis of change and motion, first at Oxford by the Merton school (Bradwardine and his followers) and later in France by Nicole Oresme, Bishop of Lisieux. Unfortunately, progress was severely handicapped until the sixteenth century, both by the backward state of mathematics generally and by failure to use it effectively in experimental science.

This failure was rectified by Galileo (1564—1642) who laid the foundations of Dynamics, or the science of bodies in motion. Although he completely neglected the subjective aspect of time, he introduced a new concept of time and its measurement by relating it to the concept of space. He endeavoured to extend the methods of Euclidean geometry to problems involving the passage of time, which he regarded as measurable by a point moving along a straight line. As points are dimensionless, this idea of time depended on the notion of the durationless instant which the Greeks had rejected on logical grounds. Excessive attention to logical perfection, however, had been responsible for their neglect of problems concerning motion.

Galileo raised the concepts of space and time to the status of fundamental categories by directing attention to the mathematical

[1] 'What then is time? If no-one asks me, I know; if I wish to explain it to one that asketh, I know not!'

description of motion. Previously these concepts had been relatively unimportant, but in the new mathematical philosophy the external world became a world of bodies moving in space and time. In the *Timaeus* Plato had expounded a theory that outside the universe, which he regarded as bounded and spherical, there was an infinite empty space. The ideas of Plato were much discussed in the middle of the seventeenth century by the Cambridge Platonists, and Newton's views were greatly influenced in consequence. He regarded space as the 'sensorium of God' and hence endowed it with objective existence, although he confessed that it could not be observed. Similarly, he believed that time had an objective existence independent of the particular processes which can be used for measuring it. In the *Principia*, published in 1687, he expressed his ideas thus:

'I. Absolute, true and mathematical time, of itself, and from its own nature, flows equably without regard to anything external, and by another name is called duration: relative, apparent and common time is some sensible and external (whether accurate or unequable) measure of duration by means of motion, which is commonly used instead of true time; such as an hour, a day, a month or a year.

'II. Absolute space, in its own nature, without regard to anything external, remains always similar and immovable. Relative space is some movable dimension or measure of the absolute spaces which our senses determine by its position to bodies, and which is vulgarly taken for immovable space; such is the dimension of a subterraneous, an aerial, or celestial space, determined by its position in respect of the earth. Absolute and relative space are the same in figure and magnitude; but they do not remain always numerically the same. For if the earth, for instance, moves, a space of our air, which relatively and in respect of the earth always remains the same, will at one time be one part of the absolute space into which the air passes; at another time it will be another part of the same, and so, absolutely understood, it will be perpetually mutable.

'III. Place is a part of space which a body takes up and is, according to the space, either absolute or relative. . . .

'IV. Absolute motion is the translation of a body from one place into another; and relative motion the translation from one relative place into another. . . .

'Absolute time, in astronomy, is distinguished from relative by the equation or correction of the vulgar time. For the natural days are truly unequal, though they are commonly considered as equal, and used for a measure of time; astronomers correct this inequality for their more accurate deducing of the celestial motions. It may be that there is no such thing as an equable motion, whereby time may be accurately measured. All motions may be accelerated and retarded; but the true or equable progress of absolute time is liable to no change. The duration or perseverance of the existence of things remains the same, whether the motions are swift or slow, or none at all: and therefore it ought to be distinguished from what are only sensible measures thereof. . . .

'As the order of the parts of time is immutable, so also is the order of the parts of space. Suppose these parts to be moved out of their places, and they will be moved (if the expression may be allowed) out of themselves. For times and spaces are, as it were, the places as well of themselves as of all other things. All things are placed in time as to order of succession; and in space as to order of situation. It is from their essence or nature that they are places; and that the primary places of things should be movable is absurd. These are, therefore, the absolute places, and translations out of those places are the only absolute motions.'

As the Austrian physicist and philosopher of science Ernst Mach pointed out over half a century ago, in these reflections Newton acted contrary to his expressed intention to reject hypotheses and only to investigate actual facts. Absolute time, absolute space and absolute motion are pure mental constructs that cannot be produced in experience. All our experimental knowledge concerns the relative positions and motions of bodies. However, Newton believed that he had observed absolute motion, and absolute motion implies absolute space and time:

'The effects which distinguish absolute from relative motion are centrifugal forces, or those forces in circular motion which produce a tendency of recession from the axis. For in a circular motion which is purely relative no such forces exist, but in a true and absolute circular motion they do exist, and are greater or less according to the quantity of the absolute motion.

'For instance. If a bucket, suspended by a long cord, is so often turned about that finally the cord is strongly twisted, then is filled with water, and held at rest together with the water; and afterwards, by the action of a second force, it is suddenly set whirling about the contrary way, and continues, while the cord is untwisting itself, for some time in this motion; the surface of the water will at first be level, just as it was before the vessel began to move; but, subsequently, the vessel, by gradually communicating its motion to the water, will make it begin sensibly to rotate, and the water will recede little by little from the middle and rise up at the sides of the vessel, its surface assuming a concave form (as I have experienced) and the swifter the motion becomes, the higher will the water rise, till at last, performing its revolutions in the same times as the vessel, it becomes relatively at rest to it. . . .'

The results of this famous experiment can be briefly summarized. When the pail beings to spin there is relative motion between the water and the pail. Gradually the water takes up the motion. Then the pail is suddenly stopped. If all motion is purely relative, there should be no physical difference between the configuration of the water at the instant when the pail begins to move and at the instant when its motion is arrested. In fact, the surface of the water is level at the former instant and concave at the latter. Newton concluded that rotation must be absolute.

Nevertheless, Newton's concept of absolute space was subject to a peculiar restriction. Following Galileo, he regarded uniform motion in a straight line as essentially relative. In controverting the arguments brought against Copernicus by those who refused to believe that the Earth could move, Galileo had pointed out that, if a ship is moving evenly with a constant velocity, it is impossible to judge from the behaviour of objects on board whether the ship is moving or not. Galileo's idea was expressed by Newton in the form: 'The motions of bodies enclosed in a given space are the same relatively to each other whether that space is at rest or moving uniformly in a straight line without circular motion.' Thus in Newtonian empty space rotation is absolute, but motion in a straight line with uniform speed is relative. In other words, experiments can be performed to detect rotation, but no corresponding mechanical test can be devised to indicate absolute uniform motion in a straight line. Absolute acceleration can also be detected because it is associated with the action of mechanical force.

At this point in Newton's theory we encounter a fundamental difficulty concerning the ultimate identification of 'uniformly moving' frames of reference, nowadays called *inertial frames*. The question of their identification is crucial because Newton's laws of motion are valid only for motion with respect to them. If motion is referred to any accelerated frame of reference, for example a laboratory on the surface of the Earth, then strictly speaking Newton's laws have to be modified accordingly because the Earth rotates on its axis and revolves around the Sun. In order to pick out the class of inertial frames, it is essential to make an absolute identification of at least one member. Then all the others can be determined for they are at relative rest or in uniform straight line motion with respect to it. But in order to make the necessary initial identification, Newton had to resort to what Weyl has called 'a hypothesis unfounded in experience and a dialectical dodge which strikes a discordant note in the midst of the magnificent and cogent inductive development of his system of the world in the third book of the *Principia*'. This hypothesis is a striking example of the submerged cosmology which underlies any branch of physical science.

Newton's hypothesis concerned what he called, following traditional terminology, 'the centre of the world'. In the universe of Ptolemy and Dante this centre was placed automatically at the centre of the Earth. In the Copernican universe this centre was placed at the Sun,[1] but once universal gravitation was postulated then this solution was no longer strictly valid, since the Sun itself must move. For, as Newton argued, 'since the Earth, the Sun and all the planets gravitate one towards another, and are therefore, according to their powers of gravity, in continual agitation, as the Laws of Motion require, it is plain that their movable centres cannot be taken for the immovable centre of the world. If that body were to be placed in the centre towards which other bodies gravitate most (according to common opinion), that privilege ought to be allowed to the Sun, but since the Sun itself is moved, a fixed point is to be chosen from which the centre of the Sun recedes least, and from which it would recede yet less if the body of the Sun were denser and

[1] To be historically precise, it was Kepler who placed the Sun at the centre of the world. According to Copernicus, the centre of the world was at the centre of the Earth's orbit and this was not strictly the Sun.

greater, and therefore less apt to be moved'. He concluded that 'the common centre of gravity of the Earth, the Sun and all the planets is to be esteemed the centre of the world'.

In other words, Newton was reduced to assuming that 'the universe', *i.e.* absolute space, must have a unique centre, that this centre must be at rest, and that it is the centre of gravity of the solar system. But in making these claims he was contradicting his own belief in the 'plurality of worlds'. This was all the more remarkable as this idea was one of the metaphysical driving forces behind the rise of modern science. Rejecting the closed terrestrially-centred universe of Aristotle and Ptolemy, thinkers as different in their general outlook as Descartes, Pascal and Newton all believed in plurality. The natural correlative of this belief was the idea that the universe has its centre everywhere.

Although this idea only began to be influential after the rise of the Copernican theory in the latter part of the sixteenth century (*De Revolutionibus* was published in 1543), it should be mentioned that a century earlier the mystically-minded neo-Platonist Cardinal Nicholas of Cusa had already described the universe as 'a sphere with its centre everywhere and circumference nowhere'. This famous saying—which may be regarded as the first formulation of the modern *cosmological principle* (*see* page 132)—has been traced by Alexandre Koyré back to the pseudo-Hermetic *Book of the XXIV Philosophers*, an anonymous compilation of the twelfth century. Cusanus' originality consisted in the 'astonishing transference to the universe of the pseudo-Hermetic characteristic of God'. The idea was rejected by Kepler who believed the Sun to be the centre of the world, but was enthusiastically adopted by Giordano Bruno, often known in his own day as Nolanus after his birthplace. In an interesting letter to Thomas Hariot from Sir William Lower, dated 21st June, 1610, there occurs the following passage: 'Wee . . . were a consideringe of Kepler's reasons by which he indeauors to overthrow Nolanus and Gilberts opinions concerninge the immensitie of the spheere of the starres and that opinion particularlie of Nolanus by which he affirmed that the eye being placed in anie parte of the universe, the apparence would be still all one as unto us here.'

To revert to Newton, we have seen that his philosophy of motion and nature contained an internal contradiction, however successful in practice his mathematical physics proved to be. The first to expose this fundamental flaw in his system was the famous philosopher Berkeley in his essay *De Motu*, published in 1721. Berkeley's whole philosophy was based on his rejection of abstract general ideas. In particular, he rejected the ideas of absolute space and time as objective realities existing independently of our perception. For him the fundamental dilemma in which Newton became entangled, concerning the identification of absolute space and of the ultimate point of reference with respect to which motion should be determined, did not exist. In his view there was no need to invoke—indeed there was a definite advantage in not invoking—the idea of space as something existing apart from our perception of bodies. Every place was relative, every motion was relative. If all bodies were destroyed we should be left with mere nothing, for all the attributes assigned to empty space are immediately seen to be privative or negative, except its extension. But this, when space is literally empty, cannot be divided or measured and so it too is effectively nothing. If there existed one 'globe' alone then no motion could be assigned to it; if two 'globes' then 'whatever we may understand by the application of forces, a circular motion of the two globes round a common centre cannot be conceived by the imagination'. At this point Berkeley made his most penetrating contribution to the problem. Instead of going on to point out that three 'globes' would permit us to consider motions in a plane and that four 'globes' would be required before we could conceive motion in three dimensions, he argued: 'But suppose that the sky of the fixed stars is created; suddenly from the conception of the approach of the globes to different parts of that sky the motion will be conceived.'

Although Berkeley partially reverted to the older view of Copernicus and Ptolemy, he spoke of the *sky* of fixed stars ('*Supponamus deinde coelum fixarum creari*'), not of the sphere as they did. He probably thought that the stars could be regarded as the (relatively) fixed lattice points of a space of reference. How up-to-date his astronomical knowledge was in 1720 we do not know, but until 1718 no one brought forward any *observational* evidence which conflicted with the traditional belief that (relative to each other) the stars were fixed. As mentioned in Chapter 1, in that year Halley discovered that Sirius, Arcturus and Aldebaran had moved since antiquity against the general background of the other stars. The problem of determining an 'ultimate' background is now recognized to be one of successive approximation, but Berkeley appears to have grasped the essential point that no *one* star should be regarded as more favoured than any other and hence that reference should be made to the framework of *all*.

For a century and a half Berkeley's suggestion does not appear to have been pursued further. It was revived in the latter part of the nineteenth century by Mach. In his classic *Science of Mechanics* he argued that the motion of a body K can only be estimated with reference to other bodies A, B, C, but since we are restricted to no one definite body as origin of reference the conviction arose that these bodies are indifferent generally.

'It might be, indeed, that the isolated bodies A, B, C . . . play a merely collateral role in the determination of the motion of the body K, and that this motion is determined by a *medium* in which K exists. In such a case we should have to substitute this medium for Newton's absolute space. Newton certainly did not entertain this idea. Moreover, it is easily demonstrable that the atmosphere is not this motion-determinative medium. We should, therefore, have to picture to ourselves some other medium, filling, say, all space, with respect to the constitution of which and its kinetic relations to the bodies placed in it we have at present no adequate knowledge. . . . The comportment of terrestrial bodies with respect to the earth is reducible to the comportment of the earth with respect to the remote heavenly bodies. When, accordingly, we say that a body preserves unchanged its direction and velocity *in space*, our assertion is nothing more or less than an abbreviated reference to the *entire universe*.'

Since in this context, Mach made no reference to Berkeley's *De Motu*, the belief became widespread that Mach originated this line of thought. Indeed, Einstein, when generalizing the idea in the form of a correlation of the laws of nature with the distribution of matter in the universe, considered it appropriate to coin the term *Mach's principle*. Nevertheless, despite his more careful and detailed treatment, Mach was anticipated by Berkeley in all essentials, including the critical discussion of Newton's analysis of rotational motion.

We have seen that Newton's greatest difficulty in isolating absolute space from other spaces was the determination of a fundamental origin of reference. Given such an origin we can conceive a multitude of spaces rotating around it, but Newton believed that empirical phenomena enabled us to decide which of all such spaces is absolute. Against this apparently impregnable bulwark of the Newtonian philosophy of space and motion Berkeley directed his fire of criticism. In *De Motu* he pointed out that the motion of the bucket in Newton's experiment is only apparently and not truly circular 'as that term is conceived by those who define the true places of bodies by the parts of absolute space, since it is strangely compounded of the motions, not alone of the bucket . . . but also of the daily motion of the earth round her own axis, of her monthly motion round the common centre of gravity of earth and moon, and of her annual motion round the sun'. He concluded that the phenomena cited by Newton merely indicate rotation relative to the other bodies of the universe and that it is unnecessary to introduce the idea of absolute space which in no way affects the senses and 'is quite useless for the distinguishing of motions'. In his discussion Mach made the same point, remarking that the only experimental method that could be imagined for testing the idea that rotational motion is relative (with respect to the universe as a whole) would be to compare Newton's experiment as he performed it with one in which the bucket is left undisturbed and the universe is made to rotate round it. The test is impossible to carry out and so we are not compelled to accept Newton's interpretation of his experiment.

A contemporary of Mach who made a noteworthy contribution to the same fundamental problem was the mathematician Carl Neumann in a famous inaugural lecture at Leipzig in 1869. For Newton's first law of motion to be meaningful he argued that there must be 'somewhere in the universe' a special body which can provide a basis for our judgments of motion and in particular for deciding when motion is, or is not, rectilinear. This body, which he called 'Alpha', must also be 'perfectly rigid'. Although he used the term 'body' (German *Körper*), he realized that a suitable set of three or more points forming a rigid configuration would suffice. Indeed 'Alpha' signified the possibility of making and using suitable observations to specify such a configuration.

The modern tendency is to seek a solution of these problems by combining Neumann's argument with that of Berkeley and Mach.

Instead, however, of referring to the stellar system, we now relate these ideas to the system of galaxies which we regard as the framework of the universe. The 'smoothed-out' universe provides a background against which rotation can be pictured as 'absolute'. The properties of rotating bodies, e.g. the flattening of the Earth at the poles and the motion of Foucault's pendulum, can be interpreted as evidence that they spin relative to the smoothed-out universe. It is therefore no longer necessary to argue with Newton that 'empty space' is directionally absolute. Moreover, inertia is not ascribed to the inherently absurd notion that a moving body can maintain its speed and direction unchanged with respect to an infinite vacuum, but to the 'pull' of the whole material universe when all local irregularities have been smoothed out. Deviations from uniform rectilinear motion are considered to be due to the irregularities of distribution in the actual universe.

Berkeley was not the only contemporary of Newton to advocate a relational theory of space and time. He was anticipated by Newton's famous rival, the German mathematician and philosopher Leibnitz (1646—1715). Like Berkeley he rejected the idea that space and time exist independently and in their own right, but his arguments were based on considerations of logic rather than of perception. He believed that laws of nature are laws of thought, but drew a distinction between truths of pure reason, which are 'necessary' because their opposites are self-contradictory, and truths of fact which are 'contingent' because only a 'sufficient' reason can be given why they should be so and not otherwise. He regarded propositions dealing with physical existence as being of this nature. Only a sufficient reason can be assigned to them because their opposites are not self-contradictory. By applying this principle, he came to the conclusion that space and time are not 'things' but orders or methods of arranging objects and events. In a letter to Clarke, the English defender of the Newtonian principles, Leibnitz wrote:

'I say then that if space were an absolute being, there would happen something for which it would be impossible that there should be a sufficient reason. . . . Space is something absolutely uniform, and without the things situated in it one point of space does not differ in any respect from another point of space. Now from this it follows that if we suppose that space is something in itself, other than the order of bodies among themselves, it is impossible that there should be a reason why God, preserving the same positions for bodies among themselves, should have arranged bodies in space thus and not otherwise, and why everything was not put the other way round (for instance) by changing east and west. But if space is nothing whatever without bodies but the possibility of placing them in it, these two conditions, the one as things are, the other supposed the other way round, would not differ from one another: their difference exists only in our chimerical supposition of the reality of space itself. . . .

'The same is true of time. Suppose someone asks why God did not create everything a year sooner; and that the same person wants to infer from that that God did something for which He cannot possibly have had a reason why He did it thus rather than otherwise, we should reply that his inference would be true if time were something apart from temporal things, for it would be impossible that there should be reasons why things should have been applied to certain instants rather than to others, when their succession remained the same. But this itself proves that instants apart from things are nothing, and that they only consist in the successive order of things; and if this remains the same, the one of the two states (for instance that in which the creation was imagined to have occurred a year earlier) would be nowise different and could not be distinguished from the other which now exists.'

These anti-Newtonian concepts of space and time played little part in the development of physics for over 200 years, and a further new idea was required before their physical, as distinct from their philosophical, significance could be appreciated: the idea of 'the observer'. This idea originated in the famous observations of Roemer in 1676, establishing that light takes time to travel. Previously, Galileo had attempted to discover if light had a finite velocity, but his experiments were too crude, consisting of simple signalling by means of a lantern on a hilltop. Roemer's method was astrononomical; he attempted to deduce the velocity of light from the observation of the eclipses of Jupiter's moons. These eclipses occur frequently, the two nearest moons to Jupiter being eclipsed during each revolution, the periods of revolution being forty-two and a half hours and eighty-five and a quarter hours respectively.

According as Jupiter and the Earth are on the same or opposite side of the Sun respectively, so the distance of Jupiter from the Earth varies by an amount which is approximately equal to the diameter of the Earth's orbit. Roemer discovered that the eclipses of Jupiter's moons were observed earlier when Jupiter was near the Earth and later when Jupiter was farther away. He suggested that this time-difference in the eclipses was equal to the time light takes to traverse the Earth's orbit. In this way he calculated the velocity of light and obtained a result of the right order of magnitude. The correct value is about 300,000 kilometres per second. According to the latest determination, it falls short of this round figure by only about 7·5 kilometres per second. This refers, of course, to light *in vacuo* (free space). The velocity in a medium is less, depending on the refractive index of the medium (and also on the wave-length of the light involved.)

Eddington has remarked that time as we now understand it was discovered by Roemer. For his discovery revealed that the world-as-seen at a given epoch depends on the location of the observer, and that there is no unique correlation between the succession of instants in our consciousness and the succession of events which we witness in the external world. The apparent order of events depends on who is observing them. For example, today we see two phenomena in the heavens: a prominence appears on the Sun and a new star flares up in one of the extragalactic nebulae; but the former event happened less than ten minutes ago, while millions of years have elapsed since the latter. It is not easy to reconcile with this situation the concept of an objective time-order existing independently of the observer.[1]

A new theory uniting the subjective and physical concepts of space and time was suggested in the latter half of the eighteenth century by Immanuel Kant. He maintained that space and time are forms of thought; they are ideas existing in our minds prior to any observation of phenomena, moulds into which we pour the data of physical experience. Thus Kant, like Berkeley, regarded space and time as subjective, i.e. dependent on the observer, but he did not

---

[1] Later we shall find that a common *cosmic time* exists for the special class of observers associated with the frames of reference defined by the local mean motion of matter at each place in the universe.

believe that these concepts were derived solely from experience. Similarly, he agreed with Leibnitz in regarding space and time as orders of phenomena, although he did not consider these orders to be objective, i.e. independent of the observer. He also retained Newton's idea of absolute space, 'not as a conception of a real object, but as a mere idea which is to serve as a rule for considering all motion therein as merely relative'. Although Kant's views had little direct influence on the development of classical physics, they had a profound effect on philosophy in general, for they focused attention, in a fundamental manner, on the role played by the observer or spectator of natural phenomena. This orientation of thought was of more lasting significance than the precise details of his philosophy.

Kant maintained that, as our idea of space is a necessity of thought, geometry or the science of space is a direct consequence of our method of reasoning. When Kant wrote, geometry was still the unique system expounded by Euclid, but in the early nineteenth century it was discovered that there are other systems of geometry which are equally valid logically. One of the basic assumptions of Euclidean geometry is the famous axiom of parallels: through any given point in space one and only one straight line can be drawn parallel to a given straight line. It had long been felt that this axiom was artificial, and numerous attempts had been made to deduce it from the other more cogent axioms of geometry. As failure followed failure, it occurred to certain geometers in the first decades of the nineteenth century, notably Lobatchewski in Russia, Gauss in Germany and Bolyai in Hungary, that it might be possible to construct valid systems of geometry to which the parallel postulate did not apply. Replacing Euclid's axiom by the postulate that an infinite number of parallels to a given line can be drawn through a given point, Lobatchewski discovered a system of geometry which is quite distinct from that of Euclid. It is now known as Lobatchewskian, or hyperbolic, geometry. As in Euclidian geometry, the total volume of space is infinite; on the other hand, the sum of the angles in a triangle is *less* than 180°, the difference depending on the size of the triangle. Some years later, another geometry was invented by the German mathematician Riemann (1826—1866) in which Euclid's parallel postulate was replaced by the axiom that there are no parallel lines. As such lines meet at infinity, it is not surprising that their absence implies the 'abolition of infinity', i.e. according to this geometry the total volume of space is finite. In this so-called *spherical space* the sum of the angles in a triangle *exceeds* 180°, the difference again depending on the size of the triangle.

During the remainder of the nineteenth century there was a fundamental difference of opinion between the philosophers and the mathematicians concerning the nature of space. The old idea that physical space exists in its own right still persisted, but the philosophers regarded it as Euclidean and believed that its geometry could be established by pure thought, while the mathematicians maintained that the geometry of physical space could only be determined empirically, for example by astronomical observation.

At the close of the century a new way to reconcile the two points of view was suggested by the French mathematician Henri Poincaré. He believed that there is no unique form of geometry which we are obliged to assign to the external world. For example, it had been suggested that the geometry of physical space could be determined, in principle, by measuring the sides and angles of triangles formed by various stars. Poincaré argued that such measurements would tell us nothing about space. Instead, they would provide us with information about the light rays travelling between the stars, but these rays need not be regarded as geometrical straight lines. We could map them in any space we cared to choose, although in some spaces we should find simpler geometrical relations associated with these rays than in others. From the various logically possible geometries, we could choose the one which was most convenient for our purpose. Poincaré believed that the axioms of geometry were neither synthetic *a priori* judgments (Kant's theory) nor experimental facts. Instead, in his view they were *conventions,* our choice among all possible conventions being guided by the experimental facts. To ask whether Euclidean (or any other) geometry is 'true' was no more defensible than to ask whether the metric system is 'true'. 'One geometry cannot be more true than another: it can only be *more convenient.*'[1]

---

[1] In fact, Poincaré was biased in favour of Euclidean geometry. This initial prejudice was more excusable when he wrote (in the first decade of this century) than it would have been later.

Nevertheless, there are greater restrictions on our freedom of choice in this matter than Poincaré seems to have realized, particularly when we come to consider cosmological problems, *i.e.* problems in which we cannot neglect the structure of physical space as a whole. Although we have abandoned the naive view that physical space *must* be Euclidean simply because there is no logical alternative, it does *not* follow that the geometrical properties of physical space are completely arbitrary. To appreciate this important point we must briefly compare the main characteristics of Euclidean space with those of other possible spaces. The concept of Euclidean space arose from applying Euclid's geometry uniformly to every position and region.[1] Euclidean space is therefore 'uniform' in the technical sense that congruent figures, e.g. triangles, can be constructed at all places in it. Moreover, it is isotropic, *i.e.* it exhibits no preferential directions, and congruent figures can be freely orientated anywhere in it. It is also continuous. However, it is not unique in these respects, for hyperbolic geometry and spherical geometry similarly give rise to continuous spaces which are also uniform and isotropic. The problem of determining all possible geometries with these properties was first studied in 1868 by the great German physiologist and physicist Helmholtz. He was led by his researches on the localization of objects in the field of vision to investigate the spaces in which the properties of rigid bodies are not affected by change of position, i.e. by translation and rotation. He was not an expert pure mathematician, but his pioneer researches were subsequently placed on a more rigorous footing by the Norwegian Sophus Lie. As a result, we now believe that there are no uniform continuous geometries other than the three already mentioned.

These geometries give rise to Euclidean, hyperbolic and spherical spaces, respectively.[2] Of these, as we have already seen, two are of

---

[1] Euclid himself never referred to Euclidean *space*. His famous textbook was partly a geometrical treatise on algebra and partly a long-winded logical discussion of the theory underlying the construction of the five regular solids which played a central role in Plato's cosmology.

[2] As is explained later in this chapter, although these geometries determine uniquely the *metrical* character of the spaces with which they are associated, there are other properties (*topological*) to be considered before a particular space is uniquely determined.

infinite extent, whereas the third is finite although unbounded.[1] Euclidean space is distinguished from the rest by the fact that it is the only one in which *similar*, as distinct from strictly congruent, figures are possible. Only in Euclidean space can we make a scale model which is *exactly* similar in shape to its prototype, *i.e.* Euclidean geometry is a geometry of absolute shapes and relative sizes. On the other hand, absolute size is a significant feature in both hyperbolic and spherical space. For with each of these spaces is associated a characteristic length, often called the *radius of curvature of space*. To illustrate this concept, consider the surface of a sphere. If the radius of the sphere is given, the size of any figure of given shape drawn on its surface is fixed. Spherical space is a three-dimensional analogue to the surface of the sphere, but it is important to realize that in it there is nothing corresponding to the inside and outside of the sphere.

Poincaré's argument that we can use any geometry we like to represent physical space although one geometry may be more convenient than another is based on the assumption that *in principle* we are free to adopt any scale of measurement whatsoever, however distorted it may appear to someone engaged in practical mensuration, e.g. a surveyor. An analogous situation occurs in mapping the Earth's surface. We can, if we wish, represent this on a plane, e.g. by Mercator's projection, but despite its convenience such a map is a definite distortion of the object it is meant to represent. Similarly, the choice of a particular space when mapping the universe may also involve a genuine distortion in the representation of physical objects; for example, when considering the construction of scale models, or the representation of an infinite universe in a finite spherical space.

Such distortions concern the metrical properties of the universe and its contents, and it can be argued, with some ingenuity, that Poincaré took full account of all such possibilities in his statement that, although any geometry may be used, not all geometries are equally convenient. Be that as it may, when we come to consider

---

[1] That is to say, if you kept moving in the same direction in this space, you would never come to an outer edge or rim but instead you would ultimately return to your starting-point, just as you would if you circumnavigated the Earth's equator.

certain non-metrical characteristics of space, its so-called *topological* properties, we find that Poincaré's argument definitely breaks down. One of the most important of these is *dimensionality*. In 1911 the Dutch mathematician L. E. J. Brouwer showed that it is impossible to establish a point-for-point correspondence between two Euclidean spaces of different dimensions which is everywhere continuous. Consequently, there is a genuine mathematical distinction between spaces of different dimensions. Instead of the dimensionality of physical space being a geometrical convention which we are free to choose, it must be regarded as an ineluctable feature of the universe. In our experience, physical space is found to be three-dimensional and so must be represented mathematically in terms of a three-dimensional geometry.

How is it that we know that physical space has this distinctive property? To answer this question, let us examine the restrictions which this property of space imposes on motion. For example, it is impossible to put a left glove on to a right hand so as to obtain a perfect fit, even assuming that both hands and gloves are of precisely the same size and shape. All hands and gloves are easily seen to be three-dimensional objects and to put a left glove successfully on a right hand the glove would have to be rotated in space of at least four dimensions. Because no one has yet succeeded in putting his left glove on to his right hand, it seems that physical space cannot have more than three dimensions.

This example shows that, although all exactly superposable bodies are congruent, i.e. have the same size and shape, not all congruent bodies are superposable. It may be argued, however, that the example of the glove is not conclusive, since it relates only to the potentialities of human beings living in a very restricted region of the universe. A more conclusive argument that space has only three dimensions comes from studying the physical and chemical properties of matter. The difference between congruent but non-superposable bodies, such as right hand and left hand, is called by crystallographers *enantiomorphism*. The fact that three-dimensional enantiomorphic spatial arrangements of the same molecules may be the sole difference between two distinct chemical compounds was first clearly shown by Pasteur in his famous researches on tartaric and paratartaric acid, and yields an even more striking proof than the case of the glove that the number of dimensions of physical space (at least in our part of the universe) is definitely limited to three.

The most far-reaching consequence of the three-dimensional character of space is its effect on the laws of nature. Gravitational force (except for certain refinements to which reference will be made in Chapter 4) diminishes inversely as the square of the distance, and so too do electrostatic and magnetostatic forces. Again, in so far as space may be assumed to be either accurately or else approximately Euclidean, the intensity of a light source diminishes with distance according to the same geometrical law. Now, in three-dimensional space, if an effect is propagated isotropically from its source, i.e. equally in all directions, then as it diffuses outwards it will be spread over successive concentric spherical surfaces. Since, according to Euclidean geometry the area of any such surface is proportional to the square of r, where r is the radius, it follows that the intensity at any point will vary inversely as the square of r. Similarly, if physical space had four dimensions we should expect the inverse *cube* law to play a central role in physics, which it does not.[1]

Dimensionality is not the only topological property of space. Another no less important characteristic of this type is *connectivity*. This concept can be illustrated by the following example: take a long narrow rectangular sheet of paper, bring the two long edges together to form a cylinder and then connect the two open ends of the cylinder by bending them together so as to form a tyre- or ring-shaped body. The closed outer surface of this ring differs from a plane and from the surface of a sphere in the following respect. Any closed ring-like curve in a plane, or on the surface of a sphere, divides the plane, or the sphere, into two parts which, in the case of a plane, we call the inside and the outside of the curve. Moreover, it is impossible to move continuously in the plane, or on the surface of the sphere, from one side of the curve to the other without crossing it. On the other hand, on the ring-shaped surface not all closed curves will divide the surface in this way. For example, consider the curve running round this surface where the two ends of the cylinder were brought together. This closed curve does *not* divide the surface into two distinct parts. All points on the surface, other than those on the curve in question, lie on the same side of the curve and we

[1] For further discussion of this question see the *Appendix*.

can pass continuously from any one point on the surface to any other without being compelled to cross this curve. In other words, on such a surface a closed curve can be drawn which has no distinct inside and outside, for the two are identical. Such a surface is said to be multiply-connected. Any multiply-connected surface can, however, be made simply-connective by making one, or more, appropriate 'cuts', e.g. the ring-like surface becomes simply-connected if we reverse the process of generating it from a flat sheet by cutting it in the appropriate way *twice*.

In three dimensions we can make a similar distinction, but spaces will now take the place of surfaces, and surfaces will correspond to curves. In particular, a closed surface, such as a sphere, will take the place of the closed curve considered above. In Euclidean space a sphere divides space into an inside and an outside, but if we in-habited a region of the universe which was multiply-connected then it might happen that the 'inside' of a sphere or other closed surface would be identical with the 'outside' so that we could move con-tinuously from a point on one side of the closed surface to a point on the other without having to pass through it.

This situation could also arise in a simply-connected space, e.g. Euclidean space, if the number of dimensions exceeded three. For, just as in three-dimensional Euclidean space we can move con-tinuously from a point outside a circle to a coplanar point inside it without crossing the circle (by moving out of the plane and then back into it), so if space had more than three dimensions then, by moving in the fourth dimension, we could travel from a point out-side any closed surface to one inside it without ever penetrating the surface. Indeed, if there were a fourth dimension of space inaccess-ible to our sense organs, then it might happen that objects could suddenly enter our world apparently from nowhere and equally suddenly disappear. Of course, we should only be conscious of the three-dimensional sections of such four-dimensional bodies as they passed through our world. A similar idea was, in fact, suggested as a serious possibility by Sir James Jeans some thirty years ago when discussing the difficulties of explaining the arms of spiral nebulae. 'The type of conjecture which presents itself,' he wrote, 'is that the centres of the nebulae are of the nature of singular points at which matter is poured into our universe from some other, and entirely extraneous, spatial dimension, so that, to a denizen of our universe, they appear to be points at which matter is continually being created.' Be this as it may, there is no purely logical (or mathematical) objection to such an idea, fantastic as it may seem.

Since the topological characteristics of space impose restrictions on what is physically possible, it follows that Poincaré was wrong in his unqualified contention that one geometry cannot be more true than another but only more convenient. All our empirical evidence is compatible with the conclusion that, in the region of the universe with which we are familiar, physical space is both three-dimensional and simply-connected. The differences between the three uniform, isotropic geometries considered above are metrical, i.e. they relate to the measurement of lengths, etc. But we can associate with each geometry 'in the large', or in other words when considering the corresponding space as a whole, different topological properties. Strictly speaking, when the concept of either Euclidean, hyperbolic or spherical space is applied to the universe, it is usually understood to be three-dimensional and simply connected. But, as we shall see in Chapter 5, the possibility has been suggested that the basic geometry of physical space, although continuous, uniform, isotropic and three-dimensional, may have a different connectivity when considered as a whole.

Unlike the topological characteristics of space, the metrical properties which we assign to it depend on a conventional factor, namely our particular choice of instruments of measurement. Many of the most familiar metrical properties of Euclidean geometry, e.g. the sum of the angles in a triangle is the same for all triangles, refer to configurations of straight lines. What are straight lines? In the physical world there are no straight lines. There are measuring rods, light rays and so forth. In other words, in Nature there are material bodies and radiation but no purely spatial entities. If we identify particular light rays with straight lines and use theodolites to measure angles, as in surveying, the metrical properties of triangles become purely empirical facts. If the sum of the angles of a triangle differs from two right-angles, then it is open to us to decide whether to replace Euclidean geometry by some other geometry or to retain Euclidean geometry and reject our original identification of light rays with straight lines.

In practical mensuration we find that there is agreement with Euclidean geometry to within the probable errors of observation and measurement. This is not surprising because it first arose as a theoretical development of practical mensuration. Nevertheless, in view of the existence of logical alternatives, we may legitimately ask why Euclidean geometry plays this key role in relation to empirical geometrical measurements. Practical geometry is based on the concept of the *rigid body* which is supposed to retain its size and shape unaltered under all physical circumstances. The 'accurate' measuring rod is such a body. In particular, it must be unaltered by changes of position and orientation. Consequently, the geometry to which it gives rise must be uniform and isotropic. If we also assume this geometry to be continuous, as we usually do, then it must be either Euclidean, hyperbolic or spherical. Whether it is possible to find such a measuring rod, and if so over how large a region of space it is applicable without distortion, are empirical questions. But if we assume that good approximations to such a rod exist within a region which, even if large in relation to our own bodies, is nevertheless minute compared either with space as a whole (if finite) or with 'large-scale' features of space (if infinite), then it inevitably follows that local geometry will be regarded as Euclidean. For both hyperbolic and spherical geometry are themselves Euclidean within any region whose linear dimensions are small compared with the radius of curvature of space.

This reduction of spatial relationships in Nature to Euclidean geometry is therefore dependent on the concept of the ideal rigid body. This and Newton's universal absolute time are the two fundamental concepts peculiarly characteristic of classical physics. They still dominate our investigations of physical phenomena on the intermediate scale, between the very large and the very small. When, however, we come to investigate events on the astronomical and cosmological scale on the one hand and on the molecular and atomic scale on the other, we find that the idea of the rigid body as the basic instrument of spatial measurement is no longer appropriate. In astronomy both the distances and the times of events are determined by the properties of light and other forms of electromagnetic radiation. As we have seen, the fact that light, like other electromagnetic effects, travels at a finite speed leads us to question the age-old belief that there is a unique time-order of events in the universe. If, instead, temporal concepts are dependent on the observer and the properties of light, it may also happen that we are led to probe further into the nature of other concepts, in particular the idea of the rigid body. This too may cause us to reconsider our conception of physical space and its geometry. Fundamental questions of this kind were 'in the air' in the latter part of the nineteenth century, but that they would involve far-reaching modifications of classical physics was first clearly realized early in the present century by Einstein when he formulated his Special Theory of Relativity in a paper published in 1905.

4

RELATIVITY

WE HAVE already mentioned that mechanical forces produce the same effects on bodies in uniform motion as on bodies which we take to be at rest. For example, any mechanical experiment performed on board a ship sailing steadily in a straight line will yield the same result as a similar experiment carried out on land. Although the Earth revolves around the Sun and the Sun moves with respect to the stars, the motion of the Earth with respect to the basic framework of the universe can be regarded as sensibly uniform during the small interval of time covered by a laboratory experiment. Hence the laws of mechanics must be the same, or very nearly the same, in all frames of reference which are in uniform relative motion; consequently, it is not possible to devise a mechanical experiment which would permit us to measure the absolute velocity of the Earth.

The great advances in optics made during the last century suggested that it might be possible to measure the absolute velocity of the Earth by an optical experiment. This was first attempted in 1887 by Michelson and Morley. Their experiment ultimately caused a revolution in our ideas of space and time. The Newtonian concept of an absolute empty space had been severely criticized by philosophers, but these criticisms had had no influence on physicists. The systematic investigation of optical and electrical phenomena in the nineteenth century, however, led to the hypothesis that space as a whole was pervaded by the ether, a medium capable of transmitting vibrations and disturbances. In the course of time some extremely curious properties were attributed to this medium. Nevertheless, it appeared to provide a fundamental frame of reference. Michelson and Morley, therefore, attempted to measure the velocity of the Earth with respect to the ether.

The theory of their experiment was simple. Assuming that light was due to vibrations set up in the ether, they believed that its velocity must be independent of the motion of the source from which it was emitted, depending only on the properties of the ether itself. A similar effect occurs when a stone is thrown into a pond. The motion of the waves set up is independent of the speed of the stone, and is determined solely by the characteristics of the pond.

In the experiment of Michelson and Morley, a source of light was placed at the junction of two equal arms arranged at right angles.[1] Mirrors were fixed at the ends of these arms so that the light could be reflected back to its source. By means of a highly accurate instrument, known as an interferometer, it was possible to detect minute differences in the times of return of these reflected rays emitted simultaneously from the source. One arm of the apparatus was placed in the direction of the Earth's rotation in its orbit and the other at right angles. If the Earth were moving through ether, the two rays should return to the source at different times. For the to and fro velocities of light relative to the arm which was pointing in the direction of the Earth's motion should differ from the velocity relative to the arm which was pointing in the transverse direction. The velocity of the Earth in its orbit relative to the Sun is about one ten-thousandth of the velocity of light, and it was calculated that the times taken to traverse the two arms should differ by at least two parts in a hundred million. The apparatus was so accurate that far smaller differences could have been detected. However, when the experiment was first performed the two rays returned simultaneously so that the velocity of the Earth was given as zero. As this unexpected result might have been due to the Earth happening to be at rest relative to the ether at that epoch, the experiment was repeated six months later when the Earth's motion in its orbit was completely reversed in direction, but again the same result was obtained. (The experiment has been repeated many times since, and under different conditions. A different type of experiment —made in 1958, with the aid of a highly accurate molecular clock known as the 'maser'—shows that the Earth's velocity with respect to the ether would have to be *less than a thousandth part of its orbital speed around the Sun!*)

[1] In the actual experiment, the arrangement of the apparatus was somewhat more complex than here described.

Numerous attempts were made to explain this failure to measure the Earth's motion through the ether.[1] Michelson himself suggested that the Earth dragged along the ether in its neighbourhood so that the velocity of the Earth with respect to the ether would appear to be zero. Abandoning the ether theory, Ritz showed in 1908 that the experiment could be explained if it were assumed that the velocity of light depended on the velocity of its source, like that of a bullet fired from an aeroplane. But this hypothesis, in turn, was contradicted by other facts; in particular, the Dutch astronomer de Sitter showed conclusively[2] five years later that the relative motion of double stars failed to produce any differential effect on the velocity of light.

A more revolutionary hypothesis was suggested in 1892 by the Irish mathematical physicist Fitzgerald. He suggested that every body moving relative to the ether automatically contracts in the direction of motion by a definite fraction depending on its velocity. Of course, for velocities which are small compared with that of light this fraction must be minute. Thus the null result of the Michelson-Morley experiment was accounted for by assuming that the difference in velocity of the two light rays was compensated by a difference in effective length of the two supposedly equal arms. This explanation, of course, could not be verified by direct measurement because every measuring rod would itself be shortened in the same way.

[1] It is both amusing and instructive to speculate on what might have happened if such an experiment could have been performed in the sixteenth or seventeenth centuries when men were debating the rival merits of the Copernican and Ptolemaic systems. The result would surely have been interpreted as conclusive evidence for the immobility of the Earth, and therefore as a triumphant vindication of the Ptolemaic system and irrefutable falsification of the Copernican hypothesis. The moral of this historical fantasy is that it is often dangerous to believe in the absolute verification or falsification of a scientific hypothesis. All judgments of this type are necessarily made in some historical context which may be drastically modified by the changing perspective of human knowledge.

[2] This has recently (1958) been disputed by Dingle. Instead, he suggests that a definitive test should be made by investigating whether the *aberrational constant* of light from distant galaxies differs—as it should on Ritz's theory, but not on Einstein's—from that of light from nearby stars. The aberrational constant is the small angle between the direction in which a telescope must be pointed to see a star and the true direction of the star. It was first determined by Bradley in 1727, and depends on the ratio of the Earth's orbital velocity to that of light (from the star). Bradley's value for the velocity of light, determined in this way, was more accurate than Roemer's.

Coming before the discovery of X-rays by Röntgen in 1895, of radioactivity by Becquerel in 1896, and of the electron by J. J. Thomson in 1897, it may justly be claimed that this strange hypothesis was the first of the post-classical concepts of modern physics. It entailed two consequences of the greatest significance: (i) the conception of a finite upper limit for all material velocities (at which length in the direction of motion appears to shrink to zero), and (ii) a drastic modification of the classical concept of a rigid body, its length being regarded no longer as an intrinsic property which is the same in all circumstances but dependent on motion relative to the observer.

The Dutch physicist Lorentz showed that the Fitzgerald hypothesis also accounted for the null results of other experiments designed to measure the Earth's motion relative to the ether. We now realize that all these experiments indicate that the laws of optical and electromagnetic phenomena must, like the laws of mechanics, be the same for all systems in uniform relative motion. This conclusion was reached by Einstein[1] in 1905, who suggested that the simplest explanation of the Michelson-Morley experiment was the hypothesis that the velocity of light is the same for all observers in uniform relative motion. This explanation was revolutionary because it was incompatible with the classical ideas of space and time. According to these, two observers in uniform relative motion cannot assign the same finite velocity to any moving object, for the respective velocities which they assign must differ by their own velocity relative to each other. Hence, on the classical concept, if light moves with a finite velocity its value cannot be the same for all observers in uniform relative motion.

As Einstein's explanation of the Michelson-Morley experiment conflicted with the classical ideas of space and time, he began with a

[1] Einstein's priority has been challenged by the late Sir Edmund Whittaker in the brilliant historical survey of modern physics given in the second volume of his *History of the Theories of Aether and Electricity*, published in 1953. Whittaker assigns priority to Poincaré and Lorentz in developing the theory which is usually associated with the name of Einstein. Their work was, however, essentially dependent on electrodynamics, whereas his was much less restricted, being based only on the fundamentals of light propagation and in no way contingent on electrodynamics or on hypotheses concerning the interactions between elementary particles.

penetrating criticism of these concepts. In particular, he rejected the notion of absolute time as it implies that a meaning can be attached automatically to the simultaneity of two events in different places. He showed conclusively that the idea of two events being simultaneous must depend on some convention of measurement, unless the two events occur at the same place.

For example, let us suppose that an explosion occurs on Mars, which is observed by an astronomer on the Earth, who records the instant when he sees the flash. If light travelled instantaneously with an infinite velocity, this instant would coincide with the time of the explosion recorded by a hypothetical observer on Mars. In this way a meaning could be attached automatically to absolute time and the simultaneity of events at different places; indeed, the classical theory is now regarded as the limiting form of Einstein's theory when the velocity of light becomes infinite. But as there is a mass of experimental evidence supporting the view that light takes a finite time to travel a definite distance, the terrestrial observer must correct the time recorded on his watch. This correction for the time taken by light to travel from Mars will depend on assumptions concerning the velocity of light and the measurement of distance. Thus the concept of a world-wide simultaneity ceases to be a primitive idea.

Although Einstein abandoned the classical concept of absolute time, he assumed that each observer possesses a unique standard of time for recording events occurring in his immediate neighbourhood. He also assumed that each observer is provided with a rigid rod for measuring lengths. At first he confined his attention to uniformly moving observers, and proved that, if each observer assigns the same constant velocity to light rays passing between them, precise relations can be deduced correlating the measurements made by any pair. According to either observer, a yard-stick or metre rod used by the other for measuring lengths in the direction of their relative motion will appear to be shorter than one used by himself. Thus Einstein deduced and reinterpreted the Fitzgerald contraction. Similarly, according to either observer, the standard clock kept by the other will appear to run slow. There will, however, be complete symmetry between the two observers, due to the initial postulate that the laws of nature have the same form for both. In particular, each observer will assign the same relative velocity to the other. This principle of complete symmetry of observers is called the Principle of Relativity, and when they are restricted to uniform relative motion the theory of their interrelations is called the Special Theory of Relativity.

If each observer assigns the velocity v to the other and c is the velocity of light, then according to either observer the length of a standard metre rod carried by the other is shortened by a factor $\sqrt{(1-v^2/c^2)}$ corresponding to the Fitzgerald contraction. For all velocities encountered in everyday life this factor is so close to unity that the difference can be neglected. Thus for the velocity of the Earth in its orbit this factor differs from unity by about one part in 200 million. Only for velocities which are not small fractions of the velocity of light will the factor differ appreciably from one. We recall that velocities of the order of two-fifths of the velocity of light have been attributed to the most distant nebulae whose spectral shifts have been measured. Even for these enormous velocities the contraction amounts only to about eight per cent. However, for velocities nearly equal to the velocity of light this factor becomes extremely important and the apparent length of a moving rod tends to zero.

Similarly, a clock carried by an observer moving with a velocity nearly equal to that of light would appear to run very slowly.[1] In fact, the velocity of light plays the role of a limiting velocity, and it is often stated that it would be impossible for an object to have a greater velocity. Of course, this is a consequence of our method of correlating measurements by two observers. For if one observer had a greater relative velocity of recession than that of light it would be impossible for him to receive a light signal from the other. Thus,

[1] In recent years there has been a striking demonstration of Einstein's prediction that the rate of a moving clock is slowed down compared with that of a stationary clock of identical construction. Certain transient fast-moving elementary particles called π-mesons are formed in the upper atmosphere as a result of cosmic-ray bombardment. The proper life-times of these particles before they spontaneously decay is less than their time of flight through the atmosphere before encountering the observational equipment of cosmic-ray physicists. This apparent contradiction can only be resolved by invoking Einstein's theory, according to which the apparent life-time of the particles is increased by a factor equal to the reciprocal of $\sqrt{(1-v^2/c^2)}$.

an observer moving in this way could not be brought within the scope of the theory.

Since the apparent length of a moving rod depends on who is observing it, we see that the Special Theory of Relativity is incompatible with the classical idea of absolute space. Similarly, the measurement of the time interval between two given events depends on who is measuring it. The time indicated by clocks in the system in which they are at rest is called the *proper time* of the system. In Lorentz's theory of the electron this proper, or local, time had already appeared as an auxiliary mathematical quantity, but he did not regard it as true physical time. In Einstein's theory, however, there is no means of isolating this time from the infinite number of equivalent local times of different moving systems. Thus Newton's idea of absolute time plays no part, and all statements concerning time have a meaning only when referred to a definite observer.

The Special Theory of Relativity automatically accounted not only for the null result of the Michelson-Morley experiment, but also explained a number of other experimental results which were difficult to incorporate in the framework of classical physics, for example, Fizeau's experiment. It had long been known that light travels through a liquid, or other material medium, with a slower speed than through ether, or empty space. In the middle of the last century the French physicist Fizeau discovered by experiment that, if the velocity of light in a particular liquid is u relative to the liquid, and if the liquid is moving with speed v along a tube, then the velocity of the light relative to the tube is less than the sum of u and v, although according to classical ideas it should be equal to this sum.

Einstein showed that this result could be immediately explained by his theory. Whereas in classical physics velocities are compounded by the ordinary law of addition, so that a man walking at three miles per hour along the corridor of a train travelling at sixty miles per hour will appear to a man standing on a station platform to be moving at sixty-three miles per hour; according to the Special Theory of Relativity he will appear to have a slightly lower velocity. Indeed, all velocities are compounded in such a way that the result-ant of any number can never exceed the velocity of light in empty space. In particular, this velocity must be unaltered when compounded with any other velocity, as it is assumed that light has the same speed relative to each uniformly moving observer.

Although in Einstein's theory each observer has his own private space and time, so that different observers assign different lengths to the same object and different measures to the interval of time between two given events, these spaces and times, as we have already remarked, are interrelated by precise equations. The mathematical form of these equations is identical with that of certain equations discovered by Lorentz, and called after him the Lorentz formulae. Einstein, of course, gave them a new and much more powerful physical interpretation. These equations are so important that we must now explain them in detail.

Consider an event, for example the outburst of a nova (a sudden cataclysmic increase in the brightness of a faint star). Suppose this event is observed from two stars in line with the nova, and suppose further that the two stars are moving uniformly with respect to each other in this line. Let the epoch at which these stars passed by each other be taken as the zero of time measurement, and let an observer A on one of the stars estimate the distance and epoch of the nova outburst to be x units of length and t units of time, respectively. Suppose the other star is moving towards the nova with velocity v relative to A. Let an observer B on this star estimate the distance and epoch of the nova outburst to be x' units of length and t' units of time, respectively. Then the Lorentz formulae, relating x' and t' to x and t, are

$$x' = \frac{x - vt}{\sqrt{(1 - v^2/c^2)}}; \quad t' = \frac{t - vx/c^2}{\sqrt{(1 - v^2/c^2)}}.$$

These formulae are, of course, quite general, applying to any event in line with two uniformly moving observers. If we let c become infinite then the ratio of v to c tends to zero and the formulae become

$$x' = x - vt; \quad t' = t.$$

Thus if, and only if, the velocity of light were infinite, would each observer assign the same epoch to the event (so many years from the instant when the observers parted company), in agreement with the Newtonian idea that time is independent of the observer. Similarly, the distances assigned by A and B to the event would differ only by the distance between A and B themselves, in accordance with the Newtonian idea of absolute space.

In 1908 the famous mathematician Minkowski made a remarkable discovery concerning the Lorentz formulae. He showed that, although each observer has his own private space and private time, a public concept which is the same for all observers can be formed by combining space and time in a particular way. If we regard an interval of time as a kind of 'distance' in the time dimension, we can convert it into a true distance by multiplying it by the velocity of light c; in other words, with any time interval we can associate a definite spatial interval, namely the distance which light can travel in empty space in that period. If, according to a particular observer, the difference in time between any two events is T, this associated spatial interval is cT. Then, if R is the space-distance between these two events, Minkowski showed that the difference of the squares of cT and R has the same value for all observers in uniform relative motion. The square root of this quantity is called the *space-time interval* between the two events. Hence, although time and three-dimensional space depend on the observer, this new concept of space-time is the same for all observers.

Minkowski's discovery provides a vivid interpretation of Einstein's ideas. We now see that, if the universe is pictured as a system of events, then the spaces and times of different observers are simply different cross-sections of this system. The space-time interval, which is the same according to all observers, is split up, owing to their different directions and speeds, into different space and time components. Weyl has commented on this idea in the following passage. 'The scene of action of reality is not a three-dimensional Euclidean space but rather a four-dimensional world in which space and time are linked together indissolubly. However deep the chasm may be that separates the intuitive nature of space from that of time in our experience, nothing of this qualitative difference enters into the objective world which physics endeavours to crystallize out of direct experience. It is a four-dimensional continuum, which is neither "time" nor "space". Only the consciousness that passes on in one portion of this world experiences the detached piece which comes to meet it and passes behind it as *history*, that is as a process that is going forward in time and takes place in space.'

Einstein's original restriction of the principle of relativity to observers in uniform relative motion was in accordance with the fundamental laws of Newtonian mechanics. Newton's first law of motion[1] stated that 'every body continues in its state of rest or uniform motion in a straight line, except in so far as it may be compelled by force to change that state'. The relations between observers in accelerated relative motion appeared to be on quite a different footing, for according to classical ideas acceleration could occur only through the action of force. In Newtonian mechanics the assumption that the laws of nature are the same for all frames of reference in uniform relative motion (inertial frames) was reconciled with the idea of absolute space by postulating that in each frame the same length is assigned to the spatial interval between any two given places. Once this postulate had been abandoned and the notion of absolute space rejected, the restriction of the principle of relativity to frames of reference, or observers, in uniform relative motion seemed artificial. For, if space and time are relative, then presumably acceleration, like velocity, should be relative too. If so, there should be some generalization of Newton's first law to include accelerated motion.

The most familiar example of acceleration in nature occurs when an object falls freely in the Earth's field. In attempting to extend the theory of relativity to embrace motions of this type, Einstein considered the case of a man experimenting on gravitation while in a lift. As long as the lift is at rest, the man can determine the strength of the gravitational field on the Earth's surface in the usual way. He finds that all objects undergo a downward acceleration of 981 centimetres per second per second until their motion is stopped by collision with other bodies or with the floor of the lift. As this acceleration is found to be the same for all bodies in the lift, the man might conclude that the lift itself is subject to an upward acceleration of 981 centimetres per second per second and that those bodies in-

[1] The law of inertia.

side the lift, which, at least during a short time, are not forced to move in the same way, obey Newton's first law of motion and remain behind until the floor of the lift collides with them.

Suppose now that the cable supporting the lift snaps so that the lift begins to fall freely in the Earth's gravitational field. Then all the bodies in the lift will undergo the same acceleration as the lift itself and consequently will be unaccelerated relative to each other. Thus to the man in the lift it will appear that the lift itself is no longer in a field of force, but is moving in accordance with Newton's first law and so is either at rest or in uniform relative motion. But a man outside the lift and at rest on the Earth's surface will interpret the situation differently. Before the cable snaps he will regard the lift as being at rest, and after it snaps he will regard it as falling with uniform acceleration. Consequently, Einstein asserted that acceleration is not absolute, as it must depend on the choice of observer.

The conclusion that acceleration is relative implies that the concept of force[1] is also relative. To illustrate this point, Einstein considered a closed box, containing an observer and apparatus, placed in a region of space where there is no gravitational field due to outside bodies. To the middle of the lid of the chest a hook is fixed and a rope is attached. A playful spirit begins pulling at the rope with a constant force, so that the box and the observer begin to move with uniformly accelerated motion. How will the observer regard the situation? The acceleration of the box will be transmitted to him by the reaction of the floor. Moreover, if he releases an object which he had been holding, the acceleration of the box will no longer be transmitted to it and it will fall to the floor with a relative acceleration. This relative acceleration will be the same for all objects. Thus it will be natural for the observer to assume that he and the box are in a uniform gravitational field similar to that which conditions existence on the Earth. Every experiment which the observer can make will confirm his belief that the chest is at rest in a gravitational field, whereas to an outside observer it will appear to be moving with uniform acceleration. We see therefore that gravitational force is relative and not absolute, depending on the choice of

[1] Strictly speaking, this discussion is confined to inertial and gravitational forces.

observer.[1] Consequently, any extension of the principle of relativity to systems in relative acceleration should yield important results concerning gravitation.

In Newton's theory of the world, space was necessarily Euclidean because no other type of geometry had then been invented. Einstein contended that, if all possible hypothetical observers can be introduced into physics, it could no longer be assumed that the geometry of space according to each observer is Euclidean. This is easily seen in the case of two coincident observers A and B whose frames of reference are in relative rotation. We suppose that a circle is drawn about each observer in the plane perpendicular to the axis of rotation of B's frame. If space is Euclidean according to A, then the ratio of the circumference of the circle to its diameter as measured by A is the well-known number π. If the circle is also measured by B, his rod will give the same length for the radius, but in measuring the circumference B will attribute the Fitzgerald contraction to A's rod,[2] and so according to B the ratio of the circumference to the diameter will not be equal to π. Hence, if Euclidean geometry applies to the space of A, it will not apply to that of B. Consequently, in creating his General Theory of Relativity, Einstein needed a more general type of geometry than that of Euclid.

The General Principle of Relativity as formulated by Einstein asserts that the laws of nature must be expressible in a form which is the same for all possible observers moving in any way and hence for the most general transformation of space and time co-ordinates. Minkowski had shown that the fundamental geometry for un-accelerated systems remote from gravitational influence is a four-dimensional space-time. Einstein extended this idea to accelerated

---

[1] This statement, which is known as Einstein's *principle of equivalence*, and the statement at the end of the previous paragraph only apply *locally* in a region where gravitational force can be regarded as effectively uniform. Formally, Einstein's principle asserts that in such a region it is always possible to choose space-time coordinates such that the effects of gravity will not appear. In short, just as Special Relativity is concerned with the effects, including the *absence* of effects (compare the 'curious incident of the dog, in the night-time', noted by Sherlock Holmes in *Silver Blaze*), of uniform *velocity*; so General Relativity is similarly concerned with those of uniform *acceleration*.

[2] Einstein *assumed* that this will happen if B's frame rotates uniformly with respect to A's.

systems. He assumed that each portion of space-time has the same magnitude for all observers or moving systems although its space and time components vary from one observer to another. He postulated that the geometry of space-time is only approximately uniform on the cosmical scale and that when 'local' phenomena, e.g. events in the solar system, are studied we must ascribe to space-time a more general non-uniform type of geometry first studied by the German mathematician Riemann. He also postulated that all gravitational motions take place along the shortest paths in space-time; these are the analogues of straight lines in Euclidean geometry. Space-time, therefore, could not be strictly uniform because, for example, the gravitational paths of planets in the field of a double star are not the same as the paths of planets revolving about a single star. In short, Einstein assumed that the geometry of any region of space-time depends on the material objects occupying that region.[1]

This idea was not entirely new. In the late nineteenth century the British mathematician Clifford had made a similar suggestion on general philosophical grounds. In his posthumous *Common Sense of the Exact Sciences*, published in 1885, there occurs the prophetic passage: 'We may conceive our space to have everywhere a nearly uniform curvature, but that slight variations of the curvature may occur from point to point, and themselves vary with the time. These variations of the curvature with the time may produce effects which we not unnaturally attribute to physical causes independent of the geometry of our space. We might even go so far as to assign to this variation of the curvature of space "what really happens in that phenomenon which we term the motion of matter".'

In developing his geometrical theory of gravitation, Einstein looked for a particular restriction on the general Riemannian geometry of space-time which, if true for any one observer, would automatically be true for all. If this restriction determined a type of Riemannian geometry in which the shortest paths could be identified with motions in gravitational fields, it could be regarded as a reformulation of the law of gravitation. Einstein succeeded in discovering a suitable condition of this type.

---

[1] It can be shown that the shortest path 'postulate' is, in fact, a logical consequence of the general equations, due to Einstein, relating the distribution of matter and the structure of space-time.

The simplest method of testing this new law of gravitation was to consider the gravitational field surrounding a single particle, as the space surrounding such a particle must be symmetrical. If we seek the shortest paths in the space-time associated with this particle, we find that they correspond very nearly to motion in an ellipse, but the ellipse itself rotates about the centre of gravitational attraction. According to Newtonian theory, if we correct the observed motions of the planets for their perturbations upon each other, we ought to obtain a stationary ellipse for the orbit of each planet with respect to the Sun. For most of the planets the Einstein deviation from elliptical orbits is extremely small, and only for one planet is the deviation sufficiently large to be regarded as a serious discrepancy with the calculations of Newtonian theory.

The orbits of the planets are in the main very nearly circular, so that it is extremely difficult to locate accurately a definite point, for example the perihelion or point nearest to the Sun. However, in the case of Mercury this is possible, and about 100 years ago the great French astronomer Leverrier, co-discoverer with Adams of the planet Neptune, claimed that there was an unexplained observed motion in the perihelion of Mercury amounting to 43 seconds of arc per century. This would correspond to a complete rotation of the whole orbit about the Sun in rather more than a million years. To explain this discrepancy between theory and observation without rejecting the Newtonian theory, Leverrier suggested that the orbit might be perturbed by another planet, Vulcan, nearer to the Sun than Mercury and hence extremely difficult to observe. Such a planet has never yet been discovered. However, Einstein showed that this hypothesis was unnecessary, as his new law of gravitation implied that the elliptical orbit of Mercury should rotate about the Sun at the rate of 42 seconds of arc per century. This explanation of the hitherto inexplicable residuum of the motion of Mercury has been generally regarded as a remarkable confirmation of Einstein's theory. For the Earth's perihelion motion the corresponding observational effect lies between about 2 and 7 seconds of arc per century; the relativity effect is nearly 4 seconds. When the gravitational theory of Mars has been placed on a sound basis it should be possible to test the relativity effect for the motion of that planet (1·35 seconds) with greater precision than has been possible for the Earth's. It may also happen that the effect will eventually be detectable in the orbits of artificial satellites.

Einstein suggested two other critical tests of the new theory. One of these concerned the spectra of stars. Since the properties of space and time depend on the properties of matter, it follows that, in a more intense gravitational field than that of the Earth, time should run at a different rate. Thus, according to the General Theory of Relativity, a natural clock on the Sun, for example a vibrating atom, should run more slowly than the corresponding clock on the Earth. This means that it sends out vibrations at a slower rate. Now the speed at which radiation, for example light, travels is measured by the product of the wave-length and the number of waves emitted in unit time, which is usually taken to be a second. If the frequency or number of waves emitted per second is reduced, then the wave-length must be correspondingly increased, and hence there must be a displacement of the spectrum.

We have already mentioned that, according to the theory of Doppler, radiation emitted by a body automatically exhibits a spectral shift if the body is moving away from the observer. The General Theory of Relativity asserts that a strong gravitational field produces a similar effect to recession. In the case of the Sun, the predicted displacement is very small, the wave-length of a typical line in the solar spectrum being increased, compared with the wave-length of the corresponding line in the laboratory, by only two parts in a million. The precise formula for the proportional increase is GM/c^2R, where G is the universal constant of gravitation,[1] M the mass of the Sun (or whatever body is producing the field), R its radius and c the velocity of light. Unfortunately, the relativity effect is difficult to disentangle from spectral shifts which might arise in other ways. A reddening of solar lines by about the correct amount has been observed only at the limb of the Sun. St. John suggested that near the centre of the disc the Einstein shift to the red is masked by Doppler shifts to the violet due to upward radial currents. Miss Adam at Oxford has shown, however, that the observed

---

[1] Newtonian gravitational force between any two particles of masses M and m respectively when their centres of gravity are at distance R apart is given by the formula GMm/R^2. (Further discussion of mass on p. 93.)

discrepancies between the theoretical shift and the observational data cannot be explained in this way.

Since the masses of nearly all stars are believed to lie within two-fifths to four times that of the Sun, no great variation in the gravitational red-shift can be expected from the mass-factor. But the Einstein effect would be considerably larger, and therefore more readily detectable, in the case of a star with a very small radius. Fortunately, Sirius has a faint companion 'white dwarf' star which is believed to be very small but extremely dense, a cubic inch containing over a ton of matter, so that its average density is more than eighty thousand times that of water. In 1925 the American astronomer Adams found an empirical shift in the spectrum of this highly compressed star which was about thirty times as great as the relativity shift predicted for the Sun. Although at the time this result was regarded as favourable to Einstein's theory (as well as confirming the theory of the structure of white dwarfs), later views concerning the masses and radii of these stars indicated that the shift observed by Adams was only about a quarter of the calculated relativity-shift. It is thought by many astronomers that the intense pressures which must prevail in these stars give rise to spectral shifts which may well swamp the relativity effect. Recently, however, Kuiper has argued that the empirical shift found by Adams was affected by scattered light from the bright component of Sirius. He claims that the correct empirical value is roughly the same as the theoretical value predicted by Einstein's formula.

It is probable that in the future this formula will be tested above the Earth with the aid of artificial satellites. At a height of 1,000 kilometres[1] there should be a *violet*-shift, i.e. increase of frequency, in any source of light or radio waves (compared with an equivalent source on the Earth's surface) of about 10^{-10} (one part in 10,000 million). This contrary effect should arise from the terrestrial source being shifted gravitationally to the red compared with a similar course farther away from the Earth's centre. This minute violet-shift will, however, have to be disengaged from the Doppler shift associated with the satellite's motion, but this should ultimately be possible. The great advantage of this test, if and when it becomes

[1] The maximum height attained by the artificial satellite projected by the Russians on 4th October, 1957.

feasible, will be that we shall have far more precise knowledge and control of all relevant factors than in the cases of the Sun and white dwarf stars.

The third test suggested by Einstein concerned the passage of light through strong gravitational fields, for his theory predicted that light should be deflected by such fields. To appreciate this test we must first introduce some additional ideas. According to Newton's second law of motion, the deviation from uniform motion, i.e. the acceleration, of a body depends on the force acting on it, and also on an inherent property of the body which is called its *inertial mass*. In Newtonian mechanics it was assumed that this quantity is fixed, irrespective of the conditions to which the body is subjected, in particular its motion. This inertial mass, which Newton called the 'quantity of matter' in a body, can be regarded as the measure of the resistance of the body to any force acting upon it.

In developing his theory of gravitation, Newton assigned to each material body another property which is called its *gravitational mass*. Gravitational mass determined the force exerted by the body on other bodies, and so its function appears to be quite distinct from that of inertial mass. Nevertheless, the two are found to be identical in magnitude. Newton made experiments to verify this remarkable equality by swinging a pendulum with a bob which could be made with different materials. The period of swing depended on the ratio of the inertial and gravitational masses of the pendulum, but in all cases it was found to be the same, thus confirming the equality of the two masses. In 1890 Eötvös made a much more refined test with the aid of a highly sensitive instrument called a torsion balance. Repeated experiments showed that inertial and gravitational mass were equal to within one part in 100 million. Einstein suggested that this was because inertia and gravitation are identical. As we have seen in the case of the man in the lift, the same phenomena can be interpreted equally well in terms of either concept. Indeed, the identity of inertial and gravitational mass is an essential condition for the validity of Einstein's principle of equivalence.

According to the Special Theory of Relativity, the velocity of a moving body is always less than the velocity of light. Since the energy of motion of a body depends on its inertial mass and its

velocity, it follows that, if the energy of a body is increased indefinitely by the continued application of a force, the inertial mass of
the body must be increased too; for, if not, the velocity would
ultimately increase indefinitely and exceed the velocity of light.
Einstein found that, corresponding to any increase in the energy
content of a body, there is an equivalent increase in its inertial mass.
Mass and energy thus appeared to be different names for the same
thing, the energy associated with a mass M being $E=Mc^2$, where c
is the velocity of light; and the mass M of a body moving with
velocity v he found to be given by the formula

$$M= \frac{m}{\sqrt{(1-v^2/c^2)}},$$

where m is the rest-mass or mass of the body as measured by an observer
with respect to whom it is at rest. This unification of the concepts of
mass and energy is the most important consequence of the Special
Theory of Relativity. It implies that matter can be regarded as
highly concentrated energy, a view which has received remarkable
confirmation in recent work on nuclear fission. The enormous
release of energy in such processes is due to the conversion of
a small quantity of mass into its equivalent amount of liberated
energy.

Since the time of Clerk Maxwell light has been regarded as a
form of electromagnetic energy. Hence it should possess inertial
mass, as is also indicated by the existence of radiation pressure; for
it has been shown experimentally that a beam of light exerts pressure
on any object on which it falls, and so the object must exert some
force on the light in order to stop it. Indeed, radiation pressure is
believed to play a preponderant role in determining the sizes of the
larger and more diffuse stars, balancing the weight of the superimposed gases. The fact that the tails of comets passing near the Sun
tend to be directed away from the Sun is also believed to be due to
the radiation pressure of sunlight on the minute particles of which
these tails are thought to be composed.

Thus there is abundant evidence that light has inertial properties.
Hence, if inertial and gravitational phenomena are always identical,

it follows that light rays must be curved in passing through gravitational fields. Detailed analysis shows that this curvature should be exceedingly minute for the gravitational fields which we can study most easily, the formula obtained by Einstein being $4GM/c^2R$ radians, i.e. $720GM/\pi c^2R$ degrees. For light rays passing very close to the Sun it should amount to about 1·75 seconds of arc. Before devising his General Theory, Einstein calculated that on the Newtonian theory of gravitation, assuming that light has mass, the corresponding displacement should be one-half this value.

The phenomenon has been tested at eclipses of the Sun. As seen from the Earth, certain stars will appear to be in the same region of the sky as the Sun at a particular epoch. When apparently very close to the Sun they will be observed only during a total solar eclipse. On various expeditions, notably those in connection with the total eclipse of 29th May, 1919, measurements were made of the positions of such stars. Although it was widely believed that the results then obtained indicated that there was a displacement which was closer to that derived from General Relativity than to that derived from the Newtonian theory, observations made at subsequent eclipses have not led to general agreement that Einstein's theory is quantitatively confirmed. At the 1952 eclipse at Khartoum the displacement obtained was 1·70±0·10 seconds. Although this result was within three per cent. of the Einstein value, owing to the poor quality of the images little weight could be assigned to it. In a report to a conference on relativity at Berne in 1955, the American astronomer Trumpler considered that the observational data were in good agreement with Einstein's theory, but further investigation will be needed before most astronomers are convinced.

Einstein drew attention to an important theoretical consequence of the bending of light rays in a gravitational field. According to the General Theory of Relativity, it appears that the law of the constancy of the velocity of light *in vacuo*, which constitutes one of the two fundamental assumptions of the Special Theory, does not apply universally. We again see that the Special Theory of Relativity is valid only as long as we can neglect the influence of gravitational fields on the phenomena considered. The Special Theory is, in fact, the limiting form of the General Theory when gravitational effects are negligible. In practice, owing to the weakness of most gravitational fields and the minute influence they exert on the transmission of light, it follows that the Special Theory is appropriate to a wide class of physical phenomena.

The Special Theory of Relativity differs in several important respects from the General Theory. It has received a considerable degree of experimental support, whereas the General Theory has a far less impressive list of crucial empirical tests to its credit. Moreover, the Special Theory has a clearer empirical foundation. We begin with measuring rods, clocks and light signals and deduce the geometry of the space-time of Minkowski, involving numbers whose physical significance is clear. On the other hand, in developing the General Theory of Relativity, we begin with an abstract geometrical assumption. The outstanding achievement of the General Theory is the reduction of gravitation to geometry, but there is an ambiguity latent in this method. Space-time is curved in the neighbourhood of material masses, but it is not clear whether the presence of matter gives rise to the curvature of space-time or whether this curvature is itself responsible for the existence of matter. Indeed, in developing the theory this ambiguity continually arises. The expressions for the energy and momentum of a given material system depend on certain numbers characterizing the structure of space-time, but these numbers in turn depend on the distribution of matter contemplated.

Furthermore, although the Special Theory of Relativity does not account for electromagnetic phenomena, it explains many of their properties. General Relativity, however, tells us nothing about electromagnetism. In Einstein's space-time continuum gravitational forces are absorbed in the geometry, but electromagnetic forces are quite unaffected. Various attempts have been made to generalize the geometry of space-time so as to produce a unified field theory incorporating both gravitational and electromagnetic forces, but since Einstein's death in 1955 it is generally agreed that all such attempts are foredoomed to failure and that a totally different line of approach (presumably involving quantum concepts, as distinct from the continuity assumptions made by Einstein) is required.

More than forty years have elapsed since the General Theory of Relativity was first formulated. This theory which at one time was thought to be based on a principle applicable to all the forces of nature now appears to be essentially a theory of gravitation, the best theory of that subject which we have. Apart from its application to local gravitational problems where, as we have seen, the distinctive observable effects are all small, the main impact of the theory has been on cosmology.

5

WORLD-MODELS (I)

> ... Or if they list to try
> Conjecture, he his Fabric of the Heav'ns
> Hath left to their dispute, perhaps to move
> His laughter at their quaint opinions wide
> Hereafter, when they come to model Heav'n
> And calculate the Starrs ...
>
> MILTON, *Paradise Lost*, viii, 75-80.

OUR direct knowledge of the universe is confined to a limited region of space and time. In order to obtain some idea of the universe as a whole we must extrapolate and construct a world-model which will reproduce satisfactorily the principal features of the observable region. It is not surprising that so far there is no sign of any general agreement concerning the method by which this immense extrapolation in space and time should be made, particularly in view of the great difficulty of obtaining reliable data and interpretations of data relating to the more distant regions that can be observed. One point, however, on which cosmologists agree is that the cross-section of the universe which can be studied by observation is neither purely spatial nor purely temporal but is a combination of the two. For the more distant galaxies are seen by us only after their light has traversed immense distances and correspondingly long times. As the propagation of light (and of other forms of electromagnetic radiation) is the basis of our empirical knowledge of the universe and as the Theory of Relativity arose from Einstein's successful attempt to develop ideas of space and time which would be consistent with modern views concerning the propagation of light, it is not surprising that his ideas have played a prominent role in cosmology. Indeed, modern theoretical cosmology originated in a famous pioneer memoir, published by Einstein in 1917, depending on certain special assumptions about the universe as a whole.

In the Middle Ages the universe was regarded as finite, with the Earth at its centre. This idea was abandoned during the Scientific Renaissance, and the universe came to be pictured as consisting of an infinitely large number of stars scattered throughout infinite Euclidean space. This conception appeared to be a necessary consequence of the theory of gravitation; for, as Newton pointed out, a finite material universe in infinite space would tend to concentrate into one massive lump. In the first of his Four Letters to Bentley, written in 1692, he said:

'It seems to me, that if the matter of our sun and planets and all the matter of the universe, were evenly scattered throughout all the heavens, and every particle had an innate gravity towards all the rest, and the whole space throughout which this matter was scattered was but finite, the matter on the outside of this space would, by its gravity, tend towards all the matter on the inside, and, by consequence, fall down into the middle of the whole space, and there compose one great spherical mass. But if the matter was evenly disposed throughout an infinite space it could never convene into one mass; but some of it would convene into one mass and some into another, so as to make an infinite number of great masses, scattered at great distances from one to another throughout all that infinite space.'

During the nineteenth century certain difficulties in this conception were revealed. In 1826 Olbers suggested that an infinity of stars of the same average brightness of the Sun would cause the sky to be infinitely bright, or at least to appear as bright as the Sun in each direction. This difficulty can be overcome if we make special assumptions, e.g. that the stars in the more remote regions of space (observed in an earlier stage of their history) are intrinsically much fainter than those in our neighbourhood, or that radiation from more remote regions is automatically reduced in brightness as compared with that from nearby regions due to some effect which increases with distance. The latter would arise if distant objects were all moving away with sufficiently large speeds, but such a systematic effect was quite unknown last century.

A further objection was pointed out by Seeliger in 1895. He

maintained that there could not be a uniform distribution of matter in the universe obeying the Newtonian inverse square law of gravitation. For on this theory the number of lines of force which come from infinity and end in a mass m is proportional to m. Now suppose the universe contains a uniform distribution of matter of density ρ. Then a sphere of volume V will enclose a mass ρV, and so the number of lines of force passing through the surface of the sphere will be proportional to ρV. But the area of the surface of the sphere is proportional to R^2 and its volume to R^3. Therefore the number of lines of force which pass through a unit area of the sphere will be proportional to ρR, and so the intensity of the gravitational field at the surface of the sphere will increase indefinitely as the sphere expands. This is impossible, since the centre of the sphere can be anywhere we choose. Seeliger suggested that this difficulty could be overcome by an *ad hoc* amendment to the Newtonian law, which is negligible except when immense distances are involved.

An interesting attempt to reconcile the idea of an infinite distribution of stars with Newtonian gravitation was made some years ago by the Swedish astronomer Charlier in terms of a model originally suggested by the eighteenth-century mathematician Lambert. In this model a certain number of stars form a nebula, or system of the first order, so many nebulae form a super-nebula, or system of the second order, and so on indefinitely. Charlier showed how such a model could be constructed, within the framework of classical theory, without encountering the difficulties indicated by Olbers and Seeliger. Nevertheless, although in recent years the view has been generally accepted that systems of the first and second order (i.e. nebulae and clusters of nebulae) exist, few astronomers have believed in the hierarchical nature of the universe, but have regarded the clusters as the largest individual units. The suggestion that third-order systems (super-clusters) exist has, however, been made by de Vaucouleurs (*see* p. 48).

In considering the structure of the universe as a whole, Einstein assumed that to a first approximation the irregularities in the distribution of matter can be neglected. Moreover, he noted that the largest velocities then assigned to stars and nebulae were very small compared with the velocity of light. In 1917, of course, the immense red-shifts of the farther nebulae were unknown. Einstein, therefore, considered a model of the universe in which matter was distributed in a uniform and continuous manner, the relative motion of the various parts being negligible. Following Seeliger, he found it impossible to imagine the system as filling the whole of Euclidean space. Also he could not regard the universe as an island in infinite space. For, by applying a well-known theorem of Boltzmann relating the densities at various points of space in which a distribution of particles is moving at random, he showed that zero density at the boundary would necessitate zero density at all points inside.

Thus it appeared to Einstein that the universe as a whole could be neither infinite nor have a finite boundary. Hence space as a whole could not be Euclidean. We have already considered a space-time in which the curvature varies from one region to another, but in constructing a model of the universe as a whole local irregularities are neglected. Thus the space-time of the model universe must have the same properties at all points. In the classical picture time and space are distinct, time being infinite in duration and space Euclidean. In devising an alternative model Einstein retained this world-wide separation of time and space, despite the fusion of the two concepts in General Relativity, but he assumed that space as a whole was of the type known as spherical.

As we saw in Chapter 3, there are three types of space which have the same properties at all points: Euclidean or 'flat' space, Lobatchewskian or hyperbolic space, and spherical space, but of these only spherical space is finite. This space is the three-dimensional equivalent of the surface of a sphere, which is unbounded, in the sense that we can move over it without coming to any edge, as we should do in the case of a disc. On the other hand, it has a finite area. In a similar fashion, spherical space is unbounded but has a finite volume. Moreover, we can take any point on the surface of the Earth as a centre on the surface. Similarly, spherical space is symmetrically disposed with respect to every constituent point. Consequently, a uniform distribution of matter in spherical space would not automatically tend to cluster around any particular point as centre because every point would be central.

In order to obtain a model of this type in accordance with General Relativity, Einstein found it convenient to modify his law of gravitation slightly by introducing an additional term involving an entirely new constant, λ, known as the *cosmical*, or *cosmological*, *constant*. In considering local gravitational problems, for example the motion of the planets around the Sun, this term can be neglected. Einstein assumed that it was significant only when considering the universe as a whole. In constructing his world-model, Einstein found that λ was equal to the reciprocal of the square of the radius. He also discovered a simple relation between the total mass M of his model and its radius R, viz.

$$GM = \tfrac{1}{2}\pi c^2 R, \qquad (1)$$

where G is the constant of gravitation and c the velocity of light. Hence the total extent of space would be determined by the quantity of matter in the world. For example, by doubling the amount of matter we would automatically double the radius. Incidentally, since the volume of spherical space is $2\pi^2 R^3$, if the average density of matter in space is ρ, then

$$R^2 = c^2/4\pi\rho G, \qquad (2)$$

indicating that the greater the density the smaller the radius. Thus in the *Einstein universe* the curvature of space as a whole depends on the amount of matter present. It follows that on this theory there would be a definite upper limit to the size of a sphere of any particular substance. For example, a sphere of water of radius about 200 million miles would fill the world. Moreover, since an increase in the average density of matter in the model would reduce the radius, we find that Einstein's universe contains as much matter as it can possibly hold for its spatial size.

Another interesting feature of the Einstein universe is that in principle it could be circumnavigated by a ray of light, although strictly speaking it contains no radiative phenomena. Various crude estimates of the time this would take have been made, but it appears unlikely that it would be less than 1,000 million years and probably several times as long. After such a time lapse the rays of light from any star would converge again at or near the starting point. Corresponding to the original star we should then see a ghost-star occupying the position where that star had been so many thousands of millions of years ago when these light rays were first emitted. In the actual universe it is unlikely that the rays would converge with sufficient accuracy. Nevertheless, it is interesing to consider the possibility that some of the stars and nebulae which we see may after all be only optical ghosts.

This possibility has, however, been regarded by many theoretical cosmologists as too paradoxical. They have, therefore, suggested that the Einstein universe should be described in terms of a variant form of spherical space known as elliptical space. This space is identical with spherical space except that it has a different topology (or connectivity) and has only half the volume of the corresponding spherical space. (Consequently, the mass of an elliptical Einstein universe of given radius R would be half that of the corresponding spherical universe.)

The difference arises in the following way. In spherical space to any point there corresponds a unique antipodal point, just as on the surface of the Earth the South Pole is antipodal to the North. But in elliptical space the connectivity is such that when you are farthest from a given point you are not at a unique point standing in the same relation to it as the South Pole does to the North, but at any point in a region analogous to the equator. On the Earth as you travel along a meridian from one pole to the other you are continually receding from the former. But in elliptical space, after passing the region bearing the same relation to your starting point as the equator does to the North Pole, you would find that you were approaching your starting point. This is perhaps a little difficult to visualize, but the following supplementary analogy may help. Take a sheet of writing paper and bring the two edges on either side together so as to form a cylinder. The metrical geometry of figures drawn on the sheet is not altered, e.g. the area of paper inside any closed curve drawn on the sheet or the length of any line drawn on it remains the same. On the other hand, the topology, or connectivity, of the sheet *as a whole* has been changed due to the fact that the two distinct lines which originally formed opposite edges have become the same line on the cylinder. *As far as this analogy applies*, spherical space may be compared with the unrolled sheet and elliptical space with the cylinder.

Various objections have been brought forward against the Einstein model. First, absolute space and time are restored for the universe as a whole. There is a given radius of the world and a *cosmic time*, so that relativity is reduced to a local phenomenon. To this objection Eddington has replied that 'the Relativity Theory is not concerned to deny the possibility of an absolute time, but to deny that it is concerned in any experimental knowledge yet found; and it need not perturb us if the conception of absolute time turns up in a new form in a theory of phenomena on a cosmical scale, as to which no experimental knowledge is yet available. Just as each limited observer has his own particular separation of space and time, so a being co-extensive with the world might well have a special separation of space and time natural to him. It is the time for this being that is here dignified by the title of "absolute".'

Second, in Einstein's revised theory of world-gravitation the total amount of matter in a world of given radius is determined by the law of gravitation. Eddington, writing on this in 1920, said: 'Some mechanism seems to be needed, whereby either gravitation creates matter, or all the matter in the world conspires to define a law of gravitation.' He then pointed out that, although he found this 'rather bewildering', it was welcomed by those who follow Mach. 'In the philosophy of Mach a world without *matter* is unthinkable. Matter in Mach's philosophy is not merely required as a test body to display properties of something already there . . . it is an essential factor in causing those properties which it is able to display. Inertia, for example, would not appear by the insertion of one test body in the world; in some way the presence of other matter is a necessary condition. It will be seen how welcome to such a philosophy is the theory that space and the inertial frame come into being with matter, and grow as it grows.'

On the other hand, with regard to the Newtonian concept of absolute rotation, Eddington admitted that Einstein's plenum does in fact provide a world-wide inertial frame, with respect to which it can be measured. Nevertheless, Eddington believed that Einstein attributed too important a role to matter, for in his universe it appears that not only the metrical properties, as in General Relativity, but the very existence of space depends upon the existence of matter. Eddington preferred to regard matter as a manifestation of the 'structure' of space-time.

A further theoretical objection, thought to be decisive, was discovered by Eddington in 1930. Einstein's world is unstable, and if it experiences a minute disturbance it will either tend to expand or contract indefinitely. Eddington therefore suggested that Einstein's model could no longer be regarded as the approximate form of the physical world when 'smoothed-out' by the statistical averaging of observations on the distribution of matter. Instead, he suggested that it represented the initial state of the universe in the remote past. Of course, if the physical world actually began in this form, there could have been no *external* physical means of disturbing it. Eddington concluded that the initial disturbance must have been due to an inherent tendency in matter to change in some way. It is not necessary to adopt this line of argument, however, in order to reject the Einstein model. Owing to local departures from strict homogeneity, the actual world cannot be *exactly* of Einstein's form. The instability of Einstein's universe indicates that, in general, a system which is nearly, but not exactly, of this form will tend to depart further and further from it with lapse of time. Consequently, Einstein's model cannot permanently represent the smoothed-out universe of nebulae. It is possible, of course, that the actual universe was much closer to this model in the remote past than it is now.[1]

Shortly after Einstein published his original memoir on cosmology in 1917, de Sitter constructed an alternative world-model, which satisfied the same laws of world-gravitation. In this model, unlike Einstein's, space-time has an intrinsic structure of its own, independent of the presence of matter. Strictly speaking, it contains neither matter nor radiation. Nebulae, if introduced into such a model, must therefore be considered as 'test particles', having no influence on the model as a whole. However, whereas a test particle in Einstein's universe will remain at rest if it has no initial motion, a similar particle introduced into *de Sitter's universe* will immediately acquire an ever-increasing velocity of recession from the observer. Moreover, in de Sitter's universe, space-time is 'hyperbolic'. There is no absolute time, and each observer will perceive an horizon at which time will appear to him to stand still, as at the Mad Hatter's tea-party where it was always six o'clock. This phenomenon, of

---

[1] It was, however, suggested by Lemaître that the Einstein configuration was an unstable equilibrium state through which the universe slowly passed in expanding from an initial 'explosive' phase of small volume and high density.

course, is only apparent, like the rainbow. At any point on the (relative) horizon the time-flux experienced there will be the same as that experienced elsewhere. Thus, in de Sitter's world there will be an *apparent* slowing-down of distant atomic vibrations, if these keep standard time. Consequently the radiation from a distant nebula will appear to be shifted towards the red, due to the increase in wavelength corresponding to the decrease in vibrational frequency. This effect, of course, will be supplemented by the Doppler effect, due to the relative recession of the nebula regarded as a test particle.

It is clear that at best de Sitter's world, like Einstein's, can be regarded only as a limiting form of the real world. In the Einstein world there is the greatest possible concentration of matter without motion. In the de Sitter world there is motion but no matter. However, with the aid of a special hypothesis due to Weyl,[1] it can be shown that a nebula introduced into the de Sitter world will exhibit a red-shift proportional to its distance, similar to Hubble's observational law. Robertson has remarked: 'We should, of course, expect that any universe which expands without limit[2] will approach the empty de Sitter case, and that its ultimate fate is a state in which each physical unit—perhaps each nebula or intimate group of nebulae— is the only thing which exists within its own observable universe.'

The models of Einstein and de Sitter are solutions of Einstein's modified gravitational equations for a world-wide homogeneous system in which the mean density is the same everywhere and does not change with lapse of time. Such models are often referred to as 'static', although strictly speaking we now realize that the de Sitter model is best regarded as the limiting form of an expanding universe in which the mean density is everywhere zero. Both models involve a positive cosmological constant λ, determining the curvature of space. If this constant is zero, we obtain a third model in classical infinite Euclidean space. This model is empty, the space-time being that of Special Relativity.

It has been shown that these are the only possible *static* world-models based on Einstein's theory. In 1922 Friedmann, a Russian meteorologist, broke new ground by investigating non-static solu-

---

[1] That the 'world-lines' of matter, i.e. the tracks in space-time, all converge towards the past.

[2] That is to say, with continual acceleration.

tions of Einstein's field equations, in which the radius of curvature of space and the mean density vary with time.[1] This possibility had already been envisaged, in a general sense, by Clifford in the eighties. He suggested that universal space might have a constant curvature which 'may change as a whole with the time. In this way our geometry based on the sameness of space would still hold good for all parts of space, but the change of curvature might produce in space a succession of apparent physical changes.' Friedmann restricted his investigations to spaces of positive curvature, i.e. closed or finite spaces, but allowed the cosmological constant to be positive, zero or negative.

Five years later, in 1927, a more vivid account of the subject was given independently by the Belgian mathematician Abbé Lemaître who worked out the astronomical consequences in considerable detail. He, too, considered only spaces of positive curvature, and it was not until 1931 that the German astronomer Heckmann pointed out that both the curvature and the cosmical constant could be positive, zero or negative.

The investigations of Friedmann and Lemaître, although studied and extended by Robertson and other mathematicians, were neglected by most astronomers until the spring of 1930 when, following Hubble's publication of the law correlating the distances and redshifts of the extragalactic nebulae, attention was directed to the construction of expanding world-models. Eddington then discovered the 'instability' of the Einstein universe, and was led to regard the real universe as a system expanding from the Einstein model as an initial state of unstable world-equilibrium between two opposing forces, namely world-gravitation and 'cosmical repulsion' depending on positive λ.[2]

The necessity for introducing the cosmical constant λ into the gravitational equations of General Relativity was originally due, as we have seen, to Einstein's assumption that *all* stellar velocities are very small compared with that of light. Once this assumption was no

[1] The resulting world-models, like Einstein's model, depend on the concept of a common *cosmic time* for all observers moving with the average speed of all matter in their vicinity.

[2] According to this conception, the universe is now expanding more rapidly than in the past, and its age is consequently greater than the value given on the hypothesis of uniform rate of expansion. Eddington estimated an age of 90,000 million years, in a memoir published in 1944, but subsequent changes in the value attributed to the rate of recession of the nebulae would tend to reduce this.

longer required, the theoretical necessity for introducing λ became much less obvious, and in 1932 Einstein and de Sitter, in a joint memoir, argued that the original objections of 1917 to a world-model of finite density in Euclidean space no longer applied if space could be regarded as expanding. As they pointed out: 'There is no direct observational evidence for the curvature, the only directly observed data being the mean density and the expansion, which latter proves that the actual universe corresponds to the non-statical case. It is therefore clear that from the direct data of observation we can derive neither the sign nor the value of the curvature, and the question arises whether it is possible to represent the observed facts without introducing the curvature at all. Historically the term containing the "cosmological constant λ" was introduced into the field equations in order to enable us to account theoretically for the existence of a finite mean density in a static universe. It now appears that in the dynamical case this end can be reached without the introduction of λ.' The *Einstein-de Sitter* model is, therefore, a homogeneous world-model of finite density, subject to the field equations of General Relativity in expanding Euclidean space. They found that, with Hubble's value for the observed rate of expansion of approximately 540 kilometres per second per megaparsec (a million parsecs), their model predicted a smoothed-out density of approximately 4×10^{-28} grammes per cubic centimetre. Although, in their view, this density 'may perhaps be on the high side, it is certainly of the correct order of magnitude and we must conclude that at the present time it is possible to represent the facts without assuming a curvature of three-dimensional space'.[1]

However, in 1935, Milne pointed out that this apparently simple world-model has a most curious property. To any observer in it the total number of nebulae which he could observe with a telescope of unlimited power would be directly proportional to the epoch of observation, so that with the march of time new nebulae would continually 'swim into his ken' and he could thus actually witness the creative process of the world out of nothing. As Milne explained, 'The mathematics is responsible for this creation of matter.' It is

---

[1] The rate of expansion in this world-model was faster in the past than now. Its age is two-thirds that of the uniformly expanding system which has the same rate of expansion at the present time.

asked to produce a finite number of observable objects in a Euclidean space, such that each is central in the field of the remainder. 'It only achieves this object by *creating* fresh particles beyond each given particle as fast as they are required; and it brings them to birth with the velocity of light. The frontier of limiting range of observability moves onward with the speed of light; it contains always the particles just being created, and it leaves in its wake a spray of decelerating newly created particles.' Milne also stressed the corresponding results for the *Friedmann-Lemaître universes*. In particular, if the cosmical constant is positive, we find a corresponding observable annihilation of matter, due to its disappearance from the field of possible observation, as it is accelerated beyond the limiting velocity of light *in vacuo*.

In the three static universes of General Relativity the cosmical constant is related to the radius of curvature R; in the Einstein model λ is equal to the reciprocal of R^2, and in the de Sitter model λ is equal to $3/R^2$. In the only other static model, that with the space-time of Special Relativity, R is infinite and λ is zero. Hence in each of these models λ has a definite physical interpretation. It is a quantity intimately related to the radius of curvature of the world, and so provides a natural unit of *length*, except in the Special Relativity case where it does not appear.

On the other hand, in those models in which the radius varies with the epoch, there is no fixed relation between the constant λ and the variable radius. The different possibilities were conveniently tabulated in 1932 by de Sitter as follows:

λ	CURVATURE		
	Negative	*Zero*	*Positive*
Negative ..	Oscillating	Oscillating	Oscillating
Zero ..	Expanding I	Expanding I	Oscillating
Positive ..	Expanding I	Expanding I	⎰ Oscillating ⎱ Expanding I ⎰ Expanding II

In the oscillating models the 'radius' increases from zero to a certain maximum value, which varies according to the model, and then decreases again to zero, the period of oscillation varying from one to another. In the expanding models of the first type (I), the radius continually increases from zero at some definite epoch and tends to infinity after an infinite lapse of time. The expanding models of the second type (II) behave in the same way, except that at the initial epoch when expansion begins the radius has a definite non-zero value which is different for each model. Incidentally, when the curvature of space is zero, so that the 'radius' is infinite, expansion simply means that the distances between all 'fixed' points embedded in the spatial plenum increase with change of epoch. Thus the plenum is like a spotted block of rubber which is being continually distended in all directions, although the size of the spots must be regarded as independent of the distention.

We see that General Relativity presents us with an almost embarrassing plethora of 'homogeneous' expanding systems. Moreover, it yields no conclusive theoretical explanation why the universe should be expanding and not contracting. Nevertheless, appeal to General Relativity or to some alternative theory is essential, because observational data alone can at most provide us with the present values of quantities such as the radius of curvature of space and not with the history of these quantities throughout time. If appeal is made to General Relativity, then for a unique determination of a homogeneous world-model we need to know three independent criteria: λ, the sign of the curvature, and its magnitude at the present epoch, i.e. the scale of the model.

Before the introduction of the 200-inch telescope, observation yielded only two independent data, viz. the present mean density in our neighbourhood and the present value of the constant of proportionality a between velocity[1] v and distance r occurring in Hubble's law, $v = ar$. (This constant is usually known as *Hubble's constant*, although the value which is now assigned to it depends on later revisions of the distance-scale.) In 1956, however, as already mentioned

---

[1] Strictly speaking, the observational data yield a relation between red-shift and apparent magnitude. From it Hubble obtained his law relating red-shift and distance. But red-shift, if due to motion, measures velocity of recession as a fraction of the velocity of light.

in Chapter 2, Humason, Mayall and Sandage published a new major survey—the first for twenty years—of apparent magnitudes and red-shifts. From their measurements relating to distant nebulae an estimate was made of a third independent datum, the coefficient β in the corrected form of Hubble's law

$$v = ar + \beta r^2 + \ldots \tag{3}$$

Knowledge of β is, in effect, equivalent to knowledge of the temporal trend of Hubble's 'constant'. According to this survey, the estimate obtained for β indicates that, on the Doppler interpretation of the red-shifts, the nebulae are not in uniform relative motion but were receding more rapidly in the past when the light left them than they are now. If this tendency has persisted throughout the whole time since the system began to expand then this period would have been less than the value given by Hubble's 'constant' on the assumption of uniform recession.[1] As Humason, Mayall and Sandage themselves frankly admit, however, their conclusions concerning the value of β must be regarded as extremely tentative, particularly in view of the great uncertainties in the determination of the distances of the more remote nebulae from the photometric data. Future work in this field may, therefore, easily lead to a drastic modification of their conclusions.[2]

Although the determination of distances is far more uncertain than the *measurement* of spectral shifts, the most crucial problem in this subject concerns the *interpretation* of the latter. Much of the objection to the Doppler interpretation associated with recessional motion has been basically psychological. Accepting the view that the system of galaxies forms the framework of the universe, many

[1] On this assumption, $r = vt$, where the time t since expansion began is the reciprocal of α. According to Sandage (1958), t is about 13·5 thousand million years ($\pm$ 4·5 thousand million years).

[2] Recently, Baum claimed that a photoelectric determination of the red-shift of a distant galaxy which he computes to be at a distance of 1,800 million light-years indicates that β is zero and recession is, therefore, uniform. In view of the uncertainties of the distance scale, this result too can only be regarded as provisional, but Baum's achievement in measuring the largest red-shift so far determined (corresponding to the enormous velocity of 120,000 kilometres per second or about two-fifths the speed of light) is remarkable.

people find difficulty in believing that this framework is expanding and moreover that the velocities attributed to the more distant nebulae, which are so very much greater than those assigned to any other astronomical bodies, can be real. If, however, astronomical velocities are expressed, not in the usual way, but in terms of the diameters of the bodies concerned, this alleged difficulty is diminished. Thus, whereas in its motion around the Sun the Earth takes about ten minutes to pass through a distance equal to its diameter, and in its motion relative to the centre of the Milky Way the Sun describes a distance equal to its diameter in about an hour and a half; a distant galaxy comparable in size to our own stellar system and receding with one-tenth of the velocity of light requires roughly a million years to pass through a distance equal to its main diameter. Although, strictly speaking, this way of looking at the problem *proves* nothing, it is a useful corrective to those who argue that the velocities in question cannot be accepted because they are 'fantastic'.

In order to test the recessional hypothesis, investigations have been made of the comparative displacement of lines in the spectrum of a given nebula. An essential feature of the Doppler effect is that, for a given source of light, the ratio of the observed wave-length of any line in the spectrum, for example the H or the K line of calcium, to the corresponding standard wave-length observed in the laboratory should be the same for all lines observed. As mentioned in Chapter 2, in most cases it is extremely difficult to obtain any data at all relating to extragalactic spectra, but in 1949 it was found that in each of the spectra of some twenty galaxies the ratio of observed to standard wave-length was constant to within a probable error of about five per cent. over a considerable range of wavelengths. In one case, where exceptional accuracy was possible, this result was established to within one per cent. between 3,400 and 6,600 angströms.[1]

Recently, due to an important development in radio-astronomy, it has become possible to extend this check to much longer wavelengths. Rather more than ten years ago the young Dutch astronomer van de Hulst calculated that the hydrogen atom should give rise to a well-defined spectral line in the radio range. Each of the two

[1] One angström equals one hundred-millionth of a centimetre.

electric charges (proton and electron) which form this atom spins like a top and in so doing generates a small magnetic field. These two fields can point in the same or in opposite directions. According to van de Hulst, if they point in the same direction then, on the average, after several million years the atom will spontaneously switch over to the state in which they point in opposite directions, at the same time emitting radiation of approximately 21 centimetres in wavelength. Despite the extremely low density of diffuse matter inside our Galaxy, about 10^{-24} grammes per cubic centimetre, the relative abundance of hydrogen is so great and the size of the system so vast that van de Hulst believed that this line should be observable. Indeed, in 1951 the 21-centimetre line from galactic hydrogen was detected in extended areas subtending large angles at the observer, thus confirming his prediction. To observe this line in distant galaxies which subtend very small angles is naturally much more difficult.[1] However, the identification, by Baade and Minkowski in 1954, of a strong radio source in Cygnus with a pair of colliding nebulae suggested that it might be possible to detect the 21-centimetre line in them and that this line might show the red-shift appropriate to objects at that distance. Optical measurements of the redshift exhibited by these nebulae, if interpreted as due to motion, indicated a velocity of recession of about 17,000 kilometres per second. The corresponding shift for a line of 21-centimetre standard wave-length is easily calculated to be about eighty megacycles per second. In 1956 a very careful investigation confirmed the existence of the line in these sources. Moreover, this line revealed the appropriate displacement (to within the probable error of measurement). We, therefore, conclude that for a given source the ratio of observed to standard wave-length has been found to be constant throughout a range of about 500,000 to 1—a highly satisfactory result. More recently, an investigation of hydrogen gas in the Coma cluster of galaxies with the 24-foot radio-telescope at Harvard's Agassiz Station Observatory showed that the red-shift of the 21-centimetre radiation corresponded to a recession velocity of 7,000 kilometres per second. Measurements of the red-shift of light from the same source yielded a velocity of 6,680 kilometres per second. Allowing

[1] Moreover, in the former case it is found 'in emission', in the latter 'in absorption'.

for the uncertainties of the measurements, the two results may be regarded as in good agreement.

Nevertheless, although the constancy of the shift-ratio throughout a given spectrum is a necessary condition which must be satisfied if the shift is to be attributed to radial motion, it is not a sufficient condition. In other words, the condition is not powerful enough to exclude every alternative hypothesis. With this consideration in mind I pointed out, in a paper published in 1954, that, if the extragalactic red-shift is due, not to relative *motion*, but to some progressive reddening effect associated with the immense *distances* between sources and observer, then, under very general conditions, we should be led to expect that the law of red-shifts would be of the form

$$z = ar + \tfrac{1}{2}(ar)^2 + \ldots, \tag{4}$$

where z denotes the fractional shift (ratio of shift of wave-length to standard wave-length for a given spectral line) and r denotes distance. When a reliable distance-scale has been established it should be possible to use (4) in order to test the hypothesis that the extragalactic nebulae are receding. For, although confirmation of (4) will not prove that the nebulae are (statistically) stationary, any significant systematic departure from (4) will be strong evidence that they are not relatively stationary and that the universe is expanding.

Important as are the data relating red-shifts and apparent magnitudes, even more fundamental for the construction of a world-model are the statistics concerning the numerical distribution of galaxies (to some specific limiting magnitude) either over the entire celestial sphere or over a random selection of comparatively small areas. The pioneer work in this field was done by Hubble in the early nineteen-thirties. He came to the conclusion that the data fitted most naturally into a static model in Euclidean space with cosmical constant zero. Hubble's conclusion, however, was based on two hypotheses of dubious validity, namely:

(1) That the average *absolute* luminosity (or magnitude) of the more distant nebulae so far observed is equal to that of the nearer nebulae;

(2) That the *apparent* luminosity of the nebulae, making due allowance for the red-shift, is proportional to the inverse square of their distances, as for stationary objects in Euclidean space.

At one time it did not appear that the first assumption was particularly serious. For, as the distances of the farthest nebulae observed were then believed to be of the order of 500 million light-years, this assumption was equivalent to postulating that the intrinsic brightness of the average nebula has not changed appreciably in the past 500 million years. For this there is some independent evidence. From fossil records it is clear that life has existed on the Earth's surface for at least an equivalent period of time to that taken by light to cover this distance. Consequently, the continual outpouring of radiation from the Sun during this time cannot have varied greatly. If the brightness of the average nebula were mainly due to stars similar to our Sun, then it could be argued with some plausibility that its absolute luminosity has remained sensibly constant over the past 500 million years. But now that more is known of the factors bearing on stellar evolution and of the great differences in the rates at which different stars expend their available stores of luminous energy, it would be rash to regard the first assumption as anything more than a highly provisional working rule.

The second assumption has long appeared to be troublesome, for the correction that would be required if space were curved, either spherically or hyperbolically, would depend on the square of the ratio of the distances of the nebulae concerned to the radius of curvature of space. That this correction is not large over the present range of observations is by no means certain. Indeed the whole subject of distance determination, which is the crux of the problem, bristles with complications, theoretical as well as practical. There is also another difficulty. In order to estimate distance from data relating to apparent magnitude, it is essential to calculate the *total* amount of radiation received from a nebula (its bolometric magnitude) from the measured amount which directly affects the photographic plate. The latter is restricted to a limited range of wavelength. The relation between photographically observed magnitude and bolometric magnitude varies with the spectral type of the source and is affected by the red-shift. The correction required to convert from one to the other is the K-term referred to in Chapter 2. Owing to our present restricted knowledge of nebular spectra any estimate of this term is fraught with uncertainty.

Although the results of Hubble's pioneer analysis of nebular counts cannot be accepted, it would be premature to adopt *on the basis of empirical counts* any specific alternative view concerning the curvature of extragalactic space and the need to retain or abandon the cosmical constant.

The most decisive result obtained in recent years in this field concerns the clustering effect. Despite the large-scale uniformity of distribution of galaxies in all regions of the sky, the small-scale distribution is anything but uniform. The nebulae tend to congregate in clusters, some in small groups of a few and others in massive systems containing hundreds and in some cases perhaps thousands of members. In 1953 Neyman and Scott, whose attention as experts in statistical theory had been drawn to this subject, published an important memoir in which they showed that the observed small-scale patchiness of distribution was not due to some selective effect of viewing associated with intervening interstellar clouds in our own galactic neighbourhood. Instead, they claimed that practically all galaxies are members of clusters and that the distribution of cluster-centres is uniformly 'random'. Hence, it seems that the clusters rather than the individual nebulae form the principal units of the world-system.

More recently, Neymann and Scott have been investigating the possibility of discriminating between rival cosmological theories by statistical analysis of counts of clusters assuming that a chance-mechanism process is responsible for their occurrence. If the universe is homogeneous and in a stationary state, e.g. if there is no systematic recessional motion, then the number of clusters in a given volume of space should be the same however far we look out into space—and in so doing look back into the past. If, however, the universe as a whole is expanding (but is homogeneous in the sense that the mean density in any region diminishes with time according to a universal law, the same for all regions), then the number of clusters observed in a given volume of space should appear to increase the farther we peer out into space and hence back into the past, i.e. a given volume of 'old' distant space should contain more clusters than the same volume of space nearby.

How can we compare the density of matter in nearby and distant space? On a photographic plate nearby clusters are superposed on more distant ones so that the images of their member galaxies are thoroughly scrambled. It is therefore extremely difficult, if not altogether impracticable, to separate individual distant clusters from nearer ones. 'However, it occurred to us,' Neymann and Scott write, 'that a statistical analysis of the plate as a whole might resolve the question. The analysis depends on the fact that any cluster at a great distance will look smaller and more tightly packed than one of the same size close by. On this basis we can picture roughly how a plate might look if it contained a disproportionate number of distant clusters.'

Briefly, the method they adopt is as follows. Each map is divided into many small squares. The galaxies in each square are counted. If a square happens to cover part of a rich cluster, it will contain substantially more than the average number of galaxies. Moreover, the adjoining squares are also likely to be at least partly within the cluster and to have a high galaxy count. The probability of high counts will decrease as we get farther from the centre of the cluster. The larger the cluster, the farther out the high count will extend. The plate is gone over square by square and correlations are computed for adjacent squares, squares once removed, and so on. These correlations, the authors claim, should provide a basis for determining the distribution of cluster sizes in space and thus deciding between opposing theories. Although the amount of work envisaged in such a programme is enormous, Neymann and Scott base their hopes for a decision on the potentialities of modern high-speed computing machines and on a new survey of galaxies which is planned with the aid of the 120-inch reflector now being installed at the Lick Observatory on Mount Hamilton in California. When the data which this instrument is expected to provide becomes available for analysis, then, they argue, 'the crucial moment will have come. Preliminary computations indicate that the 120-inch telescope is powerful enough to penetrate far enough back into time to tell which of the two categories of cosmological theories is closer to reality'.

Nevertheless, a preliminary note of warning must be sounded. The crux of the argument is the interpretation of the appearance of distant clusters. If the smaller apparent size and more closely packed internal structure of distant galaxies and clusters are assumed statistically to be purely the effects of distance, then it should be possible to determine in the way suggested whether the remoter regions of the universe contain a significantly greater concentration of matter than the nearer. If they do, then this will indicate that in the past, when the light left those distant regions, the average density of matter in space was higher than it is now; hence, the nebulae must have receded and the universe expanded. If, however, the actual sizes of clusters and concentrations of galaxies in them were statistically different in the past from the sizes and concentrations at the present time, then great caution would have to be exercised in interpreting the data and in identifying clusters. For it might easily happen that a combined space and time effect is ascribed solely to distance with the result that distances may be wrongly estimated and the density of matter in remote regions of space incorrectly calculated. Indeed, it could easily happen that the data considered in these painstaking statistical investigations might come to be interpreted as decisive evidence for the variation (or lack of variation) with time of the mean density of the universe, although the data had in fact been misinterpreted. Thus, in order to test, in the way suggested by the authors, whether the universe is expanding or in a steady state, other considerations, e.g. some hypothesis concerning cosmical evolution, *may* prove to be inevitable.

As it happens, we already have some independent evidence bearing on the question of the concentration of galaxies in clusters in the remote past. For, from the study of the individual motions of the constituents of the *Local Group* to which our own Milky Way belongs, Hubble came to the conclusion that inside this group the law of red-shifts does not apply. Thus, if red-shifts are attributed to the effect of recession, it would seem that in the Local Group any such tendency is masked by the proper motions of the nebulae within the local gravitational field. Consequently, there is no inherent systematic tendency for the Group as a whole to expand and so it might be argued that its overall size and the concentration of galaxies in it has not changed greatly with lapse of time. However, this conclusion would be invalid if in the past the Group and its constituent members had grown in size, e.g. if, as the result of gravitational attraction, surrounding matter had fallen into, and become part of, the system. Many students of the subject believe that this is essentially the mechanism by which all large aggregates of matter, such as galaxies, have been generated. It follows that, since the more distant regions are seen as they were a long time ago, then, whether or not the galaxies are receding, we should expect distant clusters to show some systematic age-difference from those nearby, unless the universe as a whole is specifically constructed so that any such effect is automatically eliminated. As we shall see in the following chapter a particular world-model has been constructed on that basis.

Before discussing this and other 'unorthodox' world-models, let us briefly consider the present position as regards those models which are based on the field equations of General Relativity. In 1955, following the completion by Humason, Mayall and Sandage of their survey of the data relating to nebular magnitude and red-shifts, H. P. Robertson, one of the leading theoretical cosmologists of our time, made the following careful assessment of the position as he saw it. Adopting Baade's revised value of Hubble's constant, he considered the family of general relativistic models characterized by a range of values of the present density ρ_0 and cosmic epoch t_0. 'You may well object,' he wrote, 'that t_0, the "age of the universe", is hardly accessible to direct observation. Yet I take it as a significant parameter because other considerations require that it lie within certain reasonable well-defined limits; it must be long enough to allow for the observed geological and cosmogonical features of our local system and yet not so long as to lead to the exhaustion of the radioactive and fusion processes taking place about us—all this, of course, on the assumption, implied in the field equations, that the total energy of the system is conserved.'

Robertson considered the possibility of rejecting the 'questionable "cosmological constant" λ, introduced but later disowned by Einstein'. Basing his calculations on the assumption that 180 kilometres per second per megaparsec is the figure for the rate of recession of the nebulae, corresponding to a value of 5·4 thousand million years for the reciprocal of Hubble's constant, he concluded that an Einstein-de Sitter universe (zero curvature as well as zero λ) is possible if the present density ρ_0 is $6·2 \times 10^{-29}$ grammes per cubic centimetre and the age is 3·6 thousand million years. Other considerations (*see* Chapter 8) suggest that this value of t_0 may be a little low. Compared with the results of observation, the value of ρ_0 is definitely on the high side. Moreover, if we accept the tentative estimate of Humason, Mayall and Sandage concerning the greater rate of expansion of the universe in the past,[1] then to retain a model with zero λ we are compelled to adopt a higher value for ρ_0 than in the Einstein-de Sitter universe and this implies a still lower value for t_0. With Sandage's new distance-scale[2] the density of the Einstein-de Sitter universe becomes about 10^{-29} grammes per cubic centimetre and the age about 9,000 million years, but the observed density is also reduced; with the additional correction suggested by de Vaucouleurs (*see* p. 48), the age would be nearer 6,000 million years.

'My general conclusion,' Robertson wrote—and I believe his words still apply—'is that there is found in the examination of the cosmological problem no compelling reason for seeking an explanation of the red-shift as other than the Doppler shift due to motion, nor for abandoning the field equations of general relativity as untenable. Nevertheless we are faced with difficulties which bid us try with open minds for new theoretical approaches.'

---

[1] The reader will recall that the rate of expansion in the Einstein-de Sitter model was greater in the past than now; but it was not as great as the Humason-Mayall-Sandage rate.

[2] Taking the rough mean value of 13·5 thousand million years for the reciprocal of Hubble's 'constant'.

6

WORLD-MODELS (II)

IN CONSTRUCTING the world-models so far described, the primary object has been to reproduce the large-scale astronomical features of the observable region. We have seen that this is not possible without some theoretical presuppositions. The present confusing situation, in which observations appear to be insufficient to isolate a unique model, is due not only to the inadequacy of the available data, but also to disagreement among the experts concerning the best choice of basic hypotheses. Unlike all other types of physical models which are concerned with only a *part* of the physical universe, a *world*-model must not only reproduce satisfactorily the relevant large-scale features of astronomical observation, but should also provide an adequate *background* for the general laws and phenomena of physics. According to the interpretation and emphasis laid upon this second requirement, different philosophies of cosmology have been formulated and various 'unorthodox' world-models have been constructed and analysed in great detail. In studying these models detailed comparison with the observed properties of stars and nebulae is, of course, ultimately essential, but the first object is usually to satisfy certain fundamental theoretical requirements. Thus, whereas in the pioneer investigations of Einstein and de Sitter, Friedmann and Lemaître, cosmology was derived from General Relativity as an extrapolation, in the work which will now be described cosmological hypotheses (often dignified by the title of 'world-principles') are axiomatic, and hypotheses or principles appropriate to local phenomena, e.g. General Relativity, are not always invoked and may even be discarded.

For reasons of space, I propose to concentrate on three different 'unorthodox' lines of approach to cosmology associated respectively with the names of Eddington, Milne, and Bondi and Gold.[1] Eddington's work stemmed from his study of General Relativity, whereas the other theories were originally developed without reference to Einstein's investigations.

Eddington's Theory

In 1922, following a pioneer suggestion made by Weyl in 1919, Eddington welcomed the possibility of a *finite* universe, as indicated by Einstein, because of the following physical argument. Among the constants of nature there is one, viz. the ratio of the electrical force to the gravitational force between two electrons, which is a very large pure number of the order of 3×10^{42}. 'It is difficult,' Eddington wrote, 'to account for the occurrence of a pure number (of order greatly different from unity) in the scheme of things; but this difficulty would be removed if we could connect it with the number of particles in the world.' Of course, this would be possible only if the number of particles were finite, as in the Einstein universe.

Two years previously, as already mentioned in Chapter 5, Eddington had found it 'very hard to accept' Einstein's model, because the total amount of matter in it is determined by the law of gravitation. This result followed from Einstein's revised law of gravitation involving the cosmical constant λ. However, in 1934 he wrote: 'The cosmical constant expresses a relation of scale between two different types of phenomena.[2] So long as it is expressed by any number, however small, the relation remains recognized. But if it is expressed by zero the relation is broken. . . . It was a defect of Einstein's original theory, first remedied by H. Weyl, that it implied the existence of an absolute standard of length—a conception as foreign to the relativistic point of view as absolute motion, absolute simultaneity, absolute rotation, etc. To set $\lambda=0$ implies a reversion to the imperfectly relativistic theory—a step which is no more to be thought of than a return to the Newtonian theory.'

We thus see that, with the development of Eddington's ideas, the *raison d'être* of the cosmical constant was transformed so that, although the same symbol λ was retained, the concept denoted was

---

[1] Interesting models have also been suggested and analysed by Dirac, Jordan and others.

[2] For example, the radius of the electron and the radius of the universe.

quite different. Supporting his predisposition towards a world-model containing a finite number of particles in a finite spherical space characterized by a cosmical constant, with a new and beautiful mathematical technique suggested by Dirac's discovery in 1928 that in the theory of the electron there arise mathematical expressions invariant under certain types of transformation which could *not* be obtained by the mathematical method (tensor calculus) employed in General Relativity, Eddington embarked upon his boldest flight of thought. His views were presented in two impressive books: *The Relativity Theory of Protons and Electrons*, published in 1936, and *Fundamental Theory*, published posthumously in 1946.

Although in its final form Eddington's theory is independent of General Relativity and is based on a new philosophy of physical measurement, the keystone of the whole structure is Einstein's idea that the world is finite. This principle guided Eddington in his initial choice of a problem which could be solved both by General Relativity and quantum mechanics, thus providing a bridge between these two great disciplines of modern theoretical physics, uniting the astronomical universe of nebulae with the atomic universe of protons and electrons. The problem concerned the equilibrium state of a radiationless self-contained system of a very large, but finite, number of particles. Regarding it as an exercise in cosmical physics, Eddington in his preliminary calculations adopted Einstein's pioneer solution of 1917, and took over the relation quoted in Chapter 5.

$$\frac{GM}{c^2} = \tfrac{1}{2}\pi R, \tag{1}$$

R being the radius and M the mass of the system, G the constant of gravitation and c the velocity of light. However, in adopting this solution, Eddington interpreted M in a special way. He regarded it as being effectively equivalent to $\tfrac{1}{2}Nm_p$, where m_p is the mass of the proton, or nucleus of the hydrogen atom, and $\tfrac{1}{2}N$ is the total number of protons in the system. For the whole system to be electrically neutral, he assumed that it also contained $\tfrac{1}{2}N$ electrons, but as the mass of a proton is about 1,840 times that of an electron, the contribution of the electrons to M can be neglected. An Einstein universe of this type Eddington eventually called a *uranoid*.

In quantum mechanics, detailed discussion of which lies outside the scope of this book, a radiationless steady system is said to be in its 'ground state', i.e. state of lowest possible energy. There is a fundamental 'exclusion principle', due to Pauli, which asserts that in any atomic system there is only one particle at any given 'energy level'. Therefore, in solving the problem of the uranoid as an exercise in atomic physics, Eddington assumed that the N particles occupied the N states of 'lowest energy'. He then found the total energy of the uranoid in terms of N and R and the constants of atomic physics. As already mentioned in Chapter 4, Einstein had shown that the mass M of a system whose total energy is E is given by the formula $E = Mc^2$. Consequently, Eddington's quantum calculation led to a second formula for the mass of the uranoid. By combining it with the first relation, he obtained two equations for the mass and radius of the uranoid in terms of the fundamental constants of nature.

This calculation was continually revised by Eddington and was eventually based on a new type of relativity theory which in its crude pioneer form was not too difficult for others to understand. The essential point in the original method, devised in 1931, was the idea that the mass of the electron was determined by its charge and by the existence of all the other particles in the uranoid. Eddington derived the relation,

$$\frac{e^2}{m_e c^2} = \frac{R}{\sqrt{N}}, \tag{2}$$

where m_e is the mass and e the charge on the electron.[1] Combining

---

[1] The expression on the left is approximately the classical 'radius of the electron'. The expression on the right was obtained by Eddington's ingenious application of Heisenberg's principle according to which there is in practice a range of uncertainty in the measurement of the position (and of the momentum) of a particle. By the theory of errors, if we have N independent particles, each with uncertainty of position R, the uncertainty of position of their mean centre is $R/\sqrt{N}$. If, instead of using one particle as an origin of reference, we use the mean of N, we obtain an origin whose uncertainty of position is $R/\sqrt{N}$. Hence, if we take the uranoid as a fundamental frame of reference, we obtain an origin whose uncertainty of position is expressible in terms of the radius of the uranoid and the number of elementary particles. This is identified with the radius of an elementary particle, e.g. an electron.

this with Eddington's form of (1), viz.,

$$\frac{GNm_p}{c^2} = \pi R,$$ (3)

we see that

$$\frac{GNm_p m_e}{e^2} = \pi \sqrt{N},$$

whence

$$N = \frac{\pi^2 e^4}{G^2 m_p^2 m_e^2}.$$ (4)

Substituting for π the well-known value 3·14 . . . , and for the other constants their centimetre-gramme-second values, viz. $G = 6·67 \times 10^{-8}$, $m_p = 1·67 \times 10^{-24}$, $m_e = 9·1 \times 10^{-28}$, $e = 4·77 \times 10^{-10}$, we find that the order of magnitude of N is 10^{-79}. *10^{79}* Consequently, the order of magnitude of M is 10^{55} grammes, or about 10^{11} times the mass of the Galaxy, and the corresponding value of R is about 1,000 million light-years.

In 1946 it was shown by the author that Eddington's order of magnitude for the mass of the universe could be obtained by a concise argument partly based on Newtonian mechanics. According to the latter, the gravitational energy of a homogeneous sphere of mass M and radius R is given by $-V$, where

$$V = \frac{3\,G\,M^2}{5\,R},$$ (5)

and G is the constant of gravitation. In general, this is very much smaller than the inertial energy assigned by Einstein,

$$E = M\,c^2,$$ (6)

where c is the velocity of light. According to Mach's principle, the inertia of a body is due to the background influence, or 'pull', of the whole universe. According to Einstein's principle of equivalence, gravitation is akin to inertia, and consequently the gravitational background influence of the whole universe should be equivalent to its inertial influence. Hence, despite the great numerical discrepancies between E and V for most physical bodies, it is suggested that, if it is legitimate to regard a certain homogeneous 'sphere' as a first approximation to the universe, then for such a sphere it is reasonable to assume that E and V are equal. This means that *the total energy of the universe is assumed to be zero.* It follows that the mass and radius must be related by the law

$$\frac{GM}{c^2} = k\,R, \tag{7}$$

where k is 5/3, or approximately 1·67. We immediately observe that this relation is identical with that characterizing the Einstein universe, except that in the latter k is $\pi/2$, or approximately 1·57. If we assume that R is of the order of 1,000 million light-years, then it follows that M is of the order of 10^{55} grammes, or 10^{79} protons or nucleons.

In Eddington's theory, the fundamental problem of whether the universe is finite or infinite is answered by exploring the consequences for physics of the assumption of finitude, rather than by an elaborate analysis of the present incomplete astronomical data. On this assumption, Eddington erected an imposing edifice of physical theory and claimed that a complete explanation of the laws of physics could be obtained thereby. He believed that the properties of matter depended on the properties of space and time, and hence on our methods of measurement. In particular he regarded N, the number of particles in the universe, as a fundamental characteristic of physical measurement which could be determined exactly by a penetrating analysis of physical theory.

We have seen that the order of magnitude of N is 10^{79}. It is readily calculated that the ratio of the radius of the proton (or electron) to the radius of the uranoid is about one part in 10^{39}. Similarly, the ratio of the gravitational force to the electrical force between a proton and an electron is also about one part in 10^{39}. The number 10^{39} is approximately the square root of N, and this suggests that these ratios are determined by the number of elementary particles in the world.

Eddington obtained precise formulae correlating the number N with many other physical constants. These depended on his *exact* evaluation of the number N. He interpreted this number as the number in spherical space of possible types of waves which, in accordance with modern atomic theory, can be associated with elementary particles. This number he ultimately evaluated by means of a development of tensor calculus suggested by Dirac's work, later supplemented by a new type of statistical relativity, as $3/2 \times 136 \times 2^{256}$, which is of the order of 10^{79}. Moreover, by adopting three standard theoretical quantities, the velocity of light, the Faraday and the Rydberg constants for hydrogen, as initial data, he claimed to have calculated correctly to one part in five thousand the values of a number of fundamental physical constants, including the constant of gravitation, Planck's constant h, and the ratio of the masses of the proton and electron.

Although it is still not possible to pass final judgment upon Eddington's work, certain features have become clearer with the passage of time. Broadly speaking, one can now assert with a fair degree of confidence that neither his general philosophy of physics[1] nor the detailed mathematical calculations by which he attained his principal results are likely to survive. In particular, his claim that many of the results of experiment and observation can be *deduced* theoretically from the way in which we measure phenomena must still be regarded as unproven. The late Sir Edmund Whittaker thought that Eddington's work should be regarded as similar to that of Archimedes in evaluating the number π, denoting the ratio of the circumference of a circle to its diameter. The ancient Egyptians were acquainted with the fact that this ratio is the same for all circles, but Archimedes showed that it could be calculated by pure theory assuming only the qualitative axioms of Euclidean geometry. Similarly, according to Whittaker, Eddington assumed various *qualitative* laws of physics, e.g. the exclusion principle already mentioned, and from them deduced *quantitative laws*, i.e. the exact values of the numbers known as the constants of nature.

However, when we come to examine the core of Eddington's

---

[1] For a brilliant and witty critical account, see Dingle's Eddington Memorial Lecture (1954) listed in the Bibliography at the end of this book.

theory, the exact determination of N, we find that he had no truly rigorous method of constructing it. Moreover, in recent years many new elementary sub-atomic particles have been discovered by experimental physicists for which there is no place in Eddington's theory. Instead then of regarding Eddington as the architect of a completed theory, he should be saluted as a pioneer whose ideas present a profound challenge to the imagination and point to a possible unification of hitherto disconnected concepts. First and foremost, his point of view was essentially *cosmological*, for instead of assuming that atomic phenomena occur in a vacuum, he invoked the whole material universe as a necessary background. Secondly, he realized that many of the results of theory and experiment are far more dependent on the way in which we measure phenomena than had been generally appreciated before. Thirdly, as we have already stressed, the keystone of Eddington's theory is his assumption that the universe is finite.

Eddington's uranoid is a static Einstein universe of hydrogen[1] at zero temperature. Such a system, as we have seen, is unstable: if submitted to a slight disturbance it will either start to expand or contract. All the available evidence indicates that we should direct our attention to the possibility of expansion. Eddington, however, assumed that expansion has a negligible effect on the 'constants of nature', which are determined by the finite static spherical uranoid. In his final paper in 1944 he estimated that at the present time the radius of the universe had expanded to about five times its initial value in the unstable Einstein state. His estimate was guided by Hubble's empirical determination of the apparent rate of recession of the nebulae as about 540 kilometres per second per megaparsec. The calculated speed of recession per unit distance in Eddington's expanding model is given by the formula

$$\frac{c}{R\sqrt{3}} \sqrt{\left(1 - \frac{3}{q^2} + \frac{2}{q^3}\right)},$$

[1] The hydrogen atom contains one proton and one electron. Recent work on the problem of the abundance of the elements indicates that hydrogen is probably the preponderant element throughout the physical universe.

I. The spiral nebula Messier 81 in Ursa Major

200-inch Hale Reflector. By courtesy of the
Mount Wilson and Palomar Observatories

11. The globular star cluster Messier 3 in Canes Venatica

200-inch Hale Reflector. By courtesy of the
Mount Wilson and Palomar Observatories

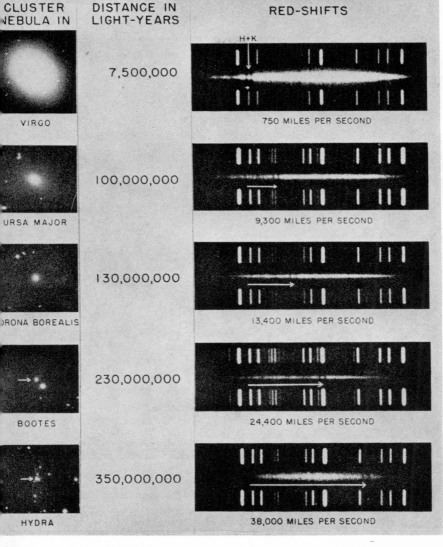

CLUSTER NEBULA IN	DISTANCE IN LIGHT-YEARS	RED-SHIFTS
VIRGO	7,500,000	H+K — 750 MILES PER SECOND
URSA MAJOR	100,000,000	9,300 MILES PER SECOND
CORONA BOREALIS	130,000,000	13,400 MILES PER SECOND
BOOTES	230,000,000	24,400 MILES PER SECOND
HYDRA	350,000,000	38,000 MILES PER SECOND

III. Relation between red-shift and distance for extra-galactic nebulae. Red-shifts are expressed as velocities. Arrows indicate shift for calcium lines H and K. The distances stated are uncorrected for the new scale factors (Baade's and Sandage's), but are probably roughly indicative of the relative distances

By courtesy of the Mount Wilson and Palomar Observatories

30"

IV. Elliptical nebula NGC 3115
By courtesy of the Mount Wilson and Palomar Observatories

v. Group of four different types of extra-galactic nebulae in Leo: elliptical, spiral and two types of barred spiral

200-inch Hale Reflector. By courtesy of the Mount Wilson and Palomar Observatories

VI. The spiral nebula NGC 4565 in Coma Berenices, seen edge on

200-inch Hale Reflector. By courtesy of the Mount Wilson and Palomar Observatories

ANDROMEDA NEBULA photographed in blue light shows giant and super-giant stars of POPULATION I in the spiral arms. The hazy patch at the upper left is composed of unresolved Population II stars.

NGC 205, companion of the Andromeda Nebula, photographed in yellow light shows stars of POPULATION II. The brightest stars are red and 100 times fainter than the blue giants of Population I.

The very bright, uniformly distributed stars in both pictures are foreground stars belonging in our own Milky Way system

VII. Stellar Populations I and II

200-inch Hale Reflector. By courtesy of the Mount Wilson and Palomar Observatories

VIII. Collision of a spiral nebula with an SO nebula, associated
with an intense radio source in Centaurus

*200-inch Hale Reflector. By courtesy of the
Mount Wilson and Palomar Observatories*

where c is the velocity of light, R the initial value of the radius before expansion begins and q the ratio of the present value of the radius to its initial value. According to this formula and Eddington's theoretical determination of R, it followed that the limiting speed of recession as q increases, viz. $c/R\sqrt{3}$, was about 572 kilometres per second per megaparsec. Hubble's result therefore indicated that q was roughly 5. In 1953, following Baade's revision of the distance-scale and the consequent drastic change in the empirical value of the rate of recession of the nebulae, N. B. Slater drew attention to a mathematical slip in Eddington's theoretical determination of R, which he had discovered some years previously, as a result of which the calculated speed of recession per unit distance had to be reduced, by multiplying it by the factor 4/9.[1] Consequently, the correct value for the limiting rate of expansion in Eddington's model is about 254 kilometres per second per megaparsec. If the present empirical value is about 180 kilometres per second per megaparsec, Eddington's value of q must be reduced to about half that which he adopted if his model is to be retained, but if a new rate of recession suggested by Sandage's work is accepted (e.g. 80 kilometres per second) then the present value of q in Eddington's model may become embarrassingly close to unity.[2]

Milne's Theory

As already stressed, according to Eddington, expansion has no effect on any of the fundamental physical constants. This point of view is in striking contrast to that of Milne, who first directed his attention to theoretical cosmology in 1932. Dissatisfied with current theories he returned to first principles, regarding expansion as the fundamental feature of the universe. He pointed out that, in general, any system of uniformly moving particles, initially distributed at

---

[1] According to Slater, his correction to Eddington's calculation of R spoiled the good agreement with the value of N as $3/2 \times 136 \times 2^{256}$, determined *a priori*, but did not affect Eddington's calculated values of the microphysical constants.

[2] This result refers only to the particular *size* of model demanded by Eddington's theory and not to all sizes of models expanding from the unstable Einstein state. Sandage's result could be taken to imply a considerably greater value of R than Eddington adopted. For further discussion of this point see the footnote on p. 145.

random in a finite region of space, would eventually be found to be receding from one another according to Hubble's relation, the fastest having travelled farthest. Compared with the actual universe, of course, such a system can only be regarded as a highly simplified model. If the nebulae are in fact all retreating from each other, it would appear that each is escaping from the gravitational field of the rest. With lapse of time their mutual gravitational attractions would steadily diminish, so that eventually the system would approximate to a set of freely moving particles exerting a negligible influence upon each other. Milne therefore thought it reasonable to assume that in this case the relative velocities would tend to become uniform. Thus, by neglecting gravitation, it should be possible to obtain some insight into the state towards which the universe is tending, and Hubble's law would appear to be its characteristic property.

If a swarm of particles expands uniformly from an initial configuration of maximum congestion, the distance travelled by each particle during time t will be the product of t and its uniform velocity. With increasing lapse of time, this product will greatly exceed the particle's initial distance from any other member of the system, and hence will become an increasingly good approximation to the actual distance. Consequently, in this case, Hubble's law will arise in a form containing a number t which can be interpreted as the 'age' of the system, different configurations corresponding to different values of t, viz. $r = vt$, or $v = r/t$.

In classical physics, most of the fundamental laws of nature were concerned either with the stability of certain configurations of bodies, e.g. the solar system, or else with the conservation of certain properties of matter, e.g. mass, energy, angular momentum or spin. The outstanding exception was the famous Second Law of Thermodynamics, discovered by Kelvin and Clausius. This law, as usually stated, refers to an abstract concept called entropy, which for any enclosed or thermally insulated system tends to increase continually with lapse of time. In practice, the most familiar example of this law occurs when two bodies are in contact: in general, heat tends to flow from the hotter body to the cooler. Thus, while the First Law of Thermodynamics, viz. the conservation of energy, is concerned only with time as mere duration, the Second Law involves the idea of trend. Milne developed his cosmology by taking this idea of trend to be fundamental, regarding the expansion of the universe as its supreme manifestation.

Having shown that Hubble's law could be immediately explained by beginning with the idea of expansion if the counteracting effect of gravitational attraction were neglected, Milne found in 1934, partly in collaboration with McCrea, that if the effect of gravitation were taken into account many of the familiar results of relativistic cosmology could be obtained using only classical ideas. In Chapter V we saw that difficulties arise if we imagine the universe to be an infinite static system in Euclidean space and subject to Newtonian gravitation. Once the possibility is admitted that the universe as a whole is not static, these objections do not necessarily apply. Milne and McCrea therefore examined the properties of an expanding universe subject to the laws of Newtonian physics. They discovered that the *local* properties of the relativistic models (with zero cosmical constant and zero pressure) in expanding spaces of positive, zero or negative curvatures are observationally the same as those of the respective Newtonian universes in which every particle has a velocity either less than the velocity of escape from the world-gravitational field in the neighbourhood of the observer, or equal to, or greater than, this velocity. Hence they considered that the idea of non-Euclidean space was not essential to our understanding of the universe.

Encouraged by these successes Milne proceeded to construct a new cosmological theory from first principles while retaining as far as possible the concept of Euclidean space. This theory was developed with particular reference to a special world-model. Following the idea suggested by his simple model of uniformly moving particles, he had already been led to consider a system of such particles which all coincide at a particular instant. This instant he regarded as the origin of time for the system. Strictly speaking, the system was assumed to exist only subsequently to this singular event which he ultimately compared to the Creation. A unique particle can be found in this model moving in any given direction with any given speed less than c, the velocity of light. Milne assumed that light rays in his model could be mapped as straight lines in Euclidean space. Thus at any epoch t, subsequent to the initial epoch zero, the system fills the *interior* of a Euclidean sphere of radius ct, the most distant particles appearing to recede with speeds arbitrarily close to c.

All the world-models which we have considered so far were based on the principle of homogeneity, each region having the same properties as any other region. Milne adopted a similar postulate for his model which was constructed so that its appearance and history were the same according to each observer attached to a constituent particle. He introduced the term *cosmological principle* to denote this hypothesis. The observers were assumed to have similar clocks, by means of which each described the system as uniformly expanding. It is clear that the system must contain an infinite number of particles, each observer mapping the system as if it were bounded at distance ct at epoch t by an impenetrable material barrier of infinite density. For, if there were only a finite number of particles inside the Euclidean sphere of radius ct, there would exist a definite rim of particles, from each of which the appearance of the system could not be the same as from an interior particle. It is of the greatest significance that the Lorentz formulae (*see* Chapter 4) do in fact permit *each* fundamental observer to describe the system as expanding equally in all directions from himself as centre. The *apparent* effect of infinite density at distance ct is due to the Fitzgerald-Lorentz 'contraction' factor, which tends to zero as the speed of recession approaches c.

In comparing this model with nature, Milne identified the constituent particles with nebulae. As in the models of relativistic cosmology, local irregularities of distribution were neglected, the model being regarded as a representation of the basic structure of the universe. For this reason, Milne called his system the *substratum*. The time-scale corresponding to uniform expansion is denoted by the symbol t. At epoch t, the distance r of a particle moving with the velocity v away from the observer is given by the relation $r = vt$. Consequently, in this model Hubble's law relating distance and velocity will be obeyed at all epochs. The present value of t, assuming the validity of Baade's distance-scale, would be between five and six thousand million years. On Sandage's new scale it might be more than twice this; but, if de Vaucouleurs' suggestion mentioned on p. 49 is also adopted, then the present value of t would lie between 7 and 10 thousand million years.

As already mentioned, Milne used his model to construct a general cosmological theory. Whereas Eddington based his cosmology on a subtle analysis of spatial measurement and regarded time as a secondary concept, Milne, believing expansion to be fundamental, developed in collaboration with me a new analysis of time and applied it to the further elucidation of his world-model. He also devised a new deductive approach to dynamics, gravitation, etc., based on certain general hypotheses. This resulting theory is called Kinematic Relativity to distinguish it from the Special and General Relativity of Einstein. In Einstein's theory the classical concepts of the rigid measuring rod and the clock are both retained, although as Poincaré pointed out in 1906 distances are judged to be equal if light-signals traverse them in equal times. This criterion is an immediate consequence of the fundamental postulate that the velocity of light *in vacuo* is the same for all uniformly moving observers. Elaborating Poincaré's point, Milne maintained that the classical concept of the rigid rod was redundant. He, therefore, proposed to base his new theory of measurement solely on the observer's awareness of the flow of time and the method of signalling, e.g. by means of light or other electromagnetic phenomena.

This policy was criticized by many authorities, including Eddington, as conflicting with the customary practice of laboratory physicists who regard length as the fundamental type of physical measurement. Nevertheless, the invention of radar has shown that Kinematic Relativity foreshadowed the most recent developments in metrology. In radar technique an estimate of the distance of a reflecting surface is provided by the time taken for a pulse of vibrations to return to the emitter, and the same principle was first suggested as the foundation of theoretical kinematics by Milne and me several years before radar was invented.

In 1933 I showed that the Lorentz formulae correlating the space and time measurements assigned to the same event by two observers in uniform relative motion could be obtained by this method without using any rigid body for measuring lengths. This was an advance on Einstein's procedure, due to its dependence on fewer basic assumptions. Not only is it independent of the idea of the rigid body, but also of the traditional implicit assumption that there is a unique scale of time in nature. Even after Einstein had discarded the idea of world-wide simultaneity, it was still thought that all natural pheno-mena suitable for use as clocks by a given observer must 'keep the same time'. For example, the daily rotation of the Earth on its axis and its annual rotation about the Sun provide two natural clocks which for most practical purposes 'keep the same time'. Milne and I, therefore, broke new ground in investigating the possibility that there might exist natural phenomena, defining physically significant time-scales, which are non-uniform when referred to the rotating Earth.

In 1936 Milne discovered a scale of time τ which could be used to construct a radar-like system of measurement so that his uniformly expanding world-model (in τ-time) could be described as static. The associated scale of spatial measurement is determined by the model itself, i.e. by the network of spatial intervals from any one constituent particle (i.e. cluster of galaxies) to any other. But if the velocity of light is still taken to be constant, the world-geometry associated with the new scale is found to be hyperbolic (Lobatchew-skian). The model fills the entire hyperbolic space, the total volume of which is infinite. Moreover, there is no origin of time on this scale, the total range of past τ-time being infinite. The infinite past on the τ-scale corresponds to the zero of time (world-creation) on the t-scale.

Milne's theory of τ-time is best regarded as a separate model from his originally uniformly expanding model, although in his own work the two were intimately associated. Milne developed a dyna-mics of the uniformly expanding model from certain basic hypo-theses, and only when this dynamics was translated into τ-time was it found to be similar to the classical dynamics of Galileo and Newton. Consequently, Milne believed τ to be the time-scale to which the swinging pendulum and the rotating Earth are found in practice to be good approximations. But in terms of the associated scale of length (assuming an invariable velocity of light) there is no systematic cosmical recession. Hence, according to Milne's τ-theory a different explanation is required to account for the red-shifts than in the case of the original uniformly expanding model. In the latter Milne followed the usual practice of identifying the uniform time of vibrations of a standard source of light of any given colour with the time of the model, which he called t-time, and so the red-shifts were explained in the orthodox way as Doppler shifts associated with recessional motion. But if standard light-pulses keep t-time (*atomic time*), the intervals between successive beats will not be uniform in τ-time (*gravitational time*). There will be a gradual increase in the frequency, or number of beats, of the light-pulse in a unit interval of τ-time and a corresponding decrease in the wavelength. Consequently, the light emitted by a standard atom in a distant nebula will appear to be redder than the light from a similar source in the laboratory because the light which we now receive from the nebula originated a long time ago when its natural wavelength was longer. Thus, according to Milne's τ-theory, the natural wave-length of any standard spectral line in the laboratory should be automatically decreasing by about one part in several thousand million (according to Sandage's revision of the distance-scale, 13,000 million) per year. This may be regarded as the central hypothesis of his τ-theory and recent developments in the construction of molecular and atomic clocks indicate that it may ultimately be possible to check this hypothesis directly. Already, however, in a paper published in 1958, D. H. Wilkinson claims that Planck's constant can change at most by one part in a million million *per annum*, whereas according to Milne's *final* view (he died in 1950) it should increase by one part in about ten thousand million, depending on the value assigned to Hubble's 'constant'.

From his cosmological hypotheses Milne attempted to deduce the fundamental laws of physics, e.g. the law of inertia, the law of gravitation, but on much of this work which is similar in nature, *mutatis mutandis*, to Eddington's Fundamental Theory, the same verdict of 'not proven' must be passed. The three main achievements of Milne's work in cosmology were: (i) the discovery of the Newtonian analogues of the various expanding world-models of relativistic cosmology; (ii) the introduction of the uniformly expanding world-model (to be distinguished from the theories of dynamics, τ-time, etc., that he afterwards elaborated with the aid of additional hypotheses); and (iii) the *idea* of different uniform time-scales operating in natural phenomena, an idea which had previously been almost entirely overlooked and certainly never systematically investigated.

The Steady-State Theory

Whereas in Milne's work primary emphasis was laid on the concept of *time* and the ruler was subordinate to the clock, in Eddington's view all physical measurements were ultimately reducible to 'pointer readings' on physical instruments of which the ruler is the prototype. Furthermore, Eddington in his analysis of General Relativity argued that matter should be regarded as the manifestation of the curvature of space-time which is, in effect, a kind of four-dimensional space, thus laying primary emphasis on the concept of *space*. In 1948 yet another world-model was constructed by Bondi and Gold, involving a new theory of *matter*.

This new model, like Milne's, is based on Mach's Principle, mentioned in Chapter 3. According to this, the laws of nature are a direct consequence of the distribution of matter in the universe. In other words, it is assumed that the contents of the universe determine its properties. This contrasts with Eddington's hypothesis that the contents of the universe are merely the material manifestation of its structure. According to the one view 'matter' is primary and determined 'form', whereas according to the other 'form' is primary and 'matter' is its manifestation. There is, however, no conclusive reason why we must adopt either of these hypotheses.

In Milne's theory, dependence of the laws of nature on the distribution of matter implies that some apparently 'invariable' relations between phenomena (e.g. the gravitational force between two given lumps of matter at a given distance apart) must slowly change with lapse of time because the universe is expanding. Bondi and Gold argue that this is an unnecessary complication and can be avoided *without sacrificing Mach's Principle*, provided it is assumed that the general distribution of matter in the universe, neglecting local irregularities, remains the same everywhere for all time. This means that the universe *as a whole* cannot be expanding, but must be in a steady state, presenting the same overall aspect from any point at any epoch. This hypothesis, which Bondi and Gold called the *Perfect Cosmological Principle*, was not in itself original. The radically new feature of their work was the combination of this hypothesis with the recessional interpretation of the extragalactic red-shifts. They argued that if the galaxies are to be regarded as mutually receding from one another and yet the overall aspect of the universe is to remain unchanged, then new galaxies must be continually in the process of formation to fill up the gaps that would otherwise arise as the older galaxies stream apart.

How can these new galaxies be generated? The only process which has been suggested as an unfailing source of supply is the continual creation of new matter. Once created, this matter is assumed to condense under mutual gravitational attraction to form new stellar systems which drift apart under the law of mutual recession. Where does this new matter come from? Bondi has answered this question unequivocally. 'It should be clearly understood,' he writes, 'that the creation here discussed is the formation of matter not out of radiation but out of nothing.' The dissipative effect of recession is exactly balanced by the continual creation of new matter *ex nihilo* so as to maintain the universe as a whole in a steady state. The required average rate of creation of new matter— it is suggested that it appears in the form of neutral hydrogen—is only one atom per litre of volume in a few thousand million years. Since it is quite impossible to observe directly such a rate of creation due to the immense volume over which a detectable amount would be spread, the authors of the theory claim that no contradiction of the observations which led Lavoisier and others to adopt the principle of the conservation of matter arises.

One of the attractive features of the new theory is that, in contrast with *most* previous theories, it yields without any additional assumptions a unique form of cosmical space-time,[1] which is the same as that of the de Sitter universe (*see* page 105). It will be remembered that in the latter the mean density of matter is zero, but that a so-called test-particle (one which has negligible influence on the model itself) introduced into it will immediately accelerate away from the observer. If we imagine such particles being continually introduced into a de Sitter model at the same uniform rate everywhere, the result will be very similar to the Bondi-Gold model, the only difference being that in the latter such particles need no longer be regarded merely as test-particles. In fact, provided that a

---

[1] Strictly speaking, the Perfect Cosmological Principle alone leads to three possibilities: (i) no recession and a changeless universe with conservation of matter; (ii) continuous creation and recession (red-shifts); (iii) continuous approach (violet-shifts) and annihilation.

uniform rate of creation is maintained at all times and places, the particles can exert their full physical effect on each other without changing the structure of de Sitter's space-time in any way. This property of de Sitter's space-time bears some resemblance to that of Minkowskian space-time, discovered by Milne some sixteen years earlier, that a world-model associated with the latter need not have zero density provided that the constituent particles recede with uniform motion from the same point-source at the same initial epoch.

Thus, the three world-models discussed in this chapter can be correlated respectively with the three possible static world-models based on Einstein's theory, referred to on page 106. However, unlike the corresponding Einstein models (i.e. those associated with the same forms of space-time), the models introduced by Milne and by Bondi and Gold are not restricted to zero-density because they are not subject to the field equations of General Relativity. These imply the temporal invariance of the constant of gravitation and the conservation of matter. Bondi and Gold accept the former but reject the latter, whereas Milne accepts the latter but rejects the former.

As mentioned in the last chapter, each observer in de Sitter's model will perceive an horizon at which time appears to him to stand still. Since the spatial and temporal properties of the Bondi-Gold model are the same as in de Sitter's, it follows that any clock associated with a receding nebula will appear to slow down in such a way that there will be a definite epoch in the history of the nebula after which no radiation emitted by the nebula can ever reach the observer. This does not mean that the galaxy suddenly disappears from view but that a finite part of its history appears to the observer to be infinitely dilated. In fact, once a particle (or galaxy) is created in the region open to possible observation by the observer (who, for the purposes of argument, is assumed to have ideally perfect instruments at his disposal), then it will never disappear from his field of view however long he may continue to make observations on the universe.

Consequently, the total amount of matter within the region open to (theoretically) possible observation must be infinite. For, if it were finite, then the continual creation of new matter in the presence of old matter which never disappears from view would be incompatible with the Perfect Cosmological Principle, according to which the overall appearance of the universe does not change with lapse of time. The total number of galaxies which will be individually visible in any potentially constructable telescope (however powerful), as distinct from an ideal telescope of unlimited power, will, however, always be finite. As the galaxies stream away from one another their relative velocities will increase asymptotically close to that of light and their spectra will be shifted farther and farther towards the far infra-red and beyond. The intensity of radiation received from these galaxies will, therefore, be much less; in other words, they will appear much fainter than if they were stationary. Consequently, only a finite number of galaxies will actually be visible in any particular telescope, but the total number in the region theoretically accessible to a telescope of unlimited power is infinite. Hence, as in Milne's uniformly expanding model, the peripheral regions will be infinitely populated by ultra-faint galaxies.

Comparison of Theories

In Milne's model all galaxies are in principle observable at any time assuming that the observer has an infinitely powerful optical or radio-telescope. Moreover, the whole model, although infinite in material content, is closed in the sense that any event occurring anywhere at any time is in principle communicable to the observer if he waits long enough to receive an optical or electro-magnetic signal. In the Bondi-Gold model, however, many galaxies will never be observable even with infinitely powerful instruments. For, consider a particular galaxy G receding from the observer O. As we have already seen, there will be a certain critical epoch in the history of G after which no signal emitted by it will ever be received by O. But, as a result of the Perfect Cosmological Principle, this epoch will be like any other in the experience of an observer on G, and later epochs will be similar to those that came earlier. Consequently, when at these later epochs the observer on G witnesses the formation of new galaxies in his neighbourhood which did not exist earlier, no information concerning these will ever be communicable to O. Thus, the Bondi-Gold steady-state model will at all times contain separate regions that cannot communicate with each other.

It is therefore not a closed system in the sense in which Milne's model is.

From the point of view of the theory of knowledge this situation is a curious one. For a galaxy which is forever beyond our range of observation, even with instruments of unlimited power, must be considered essentially unknowable. On the other hand, if one regards the model as a legitimate guide to the understanding of the structure of the universe, one must accept the Perfect Cosmological Principle and this entails, as we have seen, that entirely unknowable galaxies must exist.

This puzzling feature of the steady-state model is an extreme case of a property which is common to most models in which the rate of recession increases with time, e.g. the models of Eddington and Lemaître. In these models, as Eddington clearly recognized, there are events which can never be seen by any observer on a given nebula. One of the differences between the Einstein and de Sitter universes is that light can go right round the former but not round the latter. In an expanding universe which is on its way from the one state to the other, as Eddington believed the physical universe to be, there must be a definite moment after which circumnavigation ceases to be possible. 'It seems certain,' he wrote, 'that we are well past this moment. . . . Light is like a runner on an expanding track with the winning-post receding faster than he can run.' Somewhat later than this critical moment it becomes impossible for light to travel halfway round so that, corresponding to any star or system, there is a region of the universe which its light can now never reach. If light cannot reach it, then no other causal influence can affect it, for, as we have seen in Chapter 4, according to the theory of relativity no kind of signal can travel faster than light. 'I have sometimes pictured spherical space,' continued Eddington, 'as a bubble. Our expanding universe is an expanding bubble. It seems fair to say that when the expansion reached 1·073[1] *the bubble burst*. For regions beyond which no causal influence can ever pass are as disconnected as the fragments of a bubble.' Since matter is conserved in the expanding Eddington universe, it is only the later history of individual galaxies which is inaccessible to a particular observer, whereas in

[1] This means when the radius of the universe became 1·073 times its initial value in his theory. This number was calculated by de Sitter.

the steady-state universe with continuous creation there will be galaxies which are not accessible to observation at any stage in their history. In Eddington's (and Lemaître's) model the universe ultimately splits up into disconnected parts which are causally independent. In the Bondi-Gold theory the universe always contains infinitely many disconnected sub-universes. In Milne's model, on the other hand, *all parts* of the universe are *always* causally connected. In this respect it must be admitted that Milne's theory is the least puzzling of the three.

On the other hand, the steady-state theory has the great merit of reconciling two fundamental concepts previously regarded as incompatible: the occurrence of universal time-directed processes, e.g. the evolution of stars and galaxies and the mutual recession of nebular clusters, with the hypothesis of an unchanging general background of the universe, so that we could truly say of such a cosmos *'Plus ça change, plus ça reste la même chose !'*

In another respect, however, it can be argued that Eddington's model is preferable to Milne's and also to the steady-state model, for these imply that the universe contains an infinite amount of matter, whereas, according to Eddington the size and mass of the universe are finite. In theoretical physics the occurrence of an infinity as the result of a calculation is usually a danger signal, signifying that some concept has been stretched to bursting point. As Cardinal Nicholas of Cusa, the fifteenth-century mystical pioneer of the idea of the infinite universe, himself emphasized, there is no proportion between the finite and the infinite. The transition from the one to the other may be qualitative as well as quantitative, e.g. in the sense in which Leibnitz spoke of a living organism as an 'infinite machine'. On the other hand, the infinite is often a useful device by which we bridge the gap between two concepts, e.g. when we regard a continuous line as consisting of an infinity of points. The *mathematical infinite* as it occurs in our study of the physical world therefore plays a dual role: as a danger signal and as an intellectual tool. Nevertheless, advances in our understanding of natural phenomena have often been accompanied by the elimination of one *physical infinite* after another. In the late seventeenth century, the velocity of light was shown to be finite; this ultimately led to the theory of relativity and the conclusion that there is an upper limit to all velocities of material bodies and signals. The Aristotelian idea of the infinite divisibility of matter came to be replaced by the concepts of molecules and atoms and later by the electron, proton, neutron and other elementary particles. In the present century the rejection of the idea of the infinite divisiblity of energy has given rise to the quantum theory. Thus, there has been a 'general retreat of physical infinites' as science has advanced.[1] Einstein's discovery in 1917 of the finite universe which bears his name was in line with this development.

Although we cannot use this general argument to *prove* that the universe must be finite, the case for this conclusion is strengthened by the following consideration. Whatever may have been the precise combination of material particles that initially gave rise to the solar system, the probability of the natural occurrence of such a system, however small, is greater than zero. Consequently, in an infinite universe such a system may be expected to be repeated and in fact to occur infinitely often. Indeed, except possibly for the occurrence of life and its effects on the surface of the Earth, the *precise configuration of particles* which constitutes the solar system as it is at this particular instant of time will occur infinitely often. (Moreover, if human life and all its products were completely explicable in purely physical terms, it could be asserted that there would be infinitely many repetitions of this book, complete with plates and binding and even containing the same mistakes and misprints!) Although there is no logical objection to the possible occurrence of an infinite set of identical images of the solar system (or of this book), scepticism concerning the possible infinity of the universe is pardonable.

World-Models and World-Gravitation

Turning now to a comparison of the respective gravitational properties of the different theories under discussion, in Eddington's model gravitation is supplemented by the 'force' of cosmical repulsion. When physicists began to study the properties of atomic nuclei they were led to consider peculiar forces effective only on the nuclear scale. Similarly, it is not unreasonable to envisage the

---

[1] A notable exception to this rule would seem to be provided by the infinite universe of Digges, Bruno and Newton, but the difficulties associated with that concept were pointed out in the nineteenth century (*see* Chapter 5).

possibility of other forces of nature which are effective only on the cosmical scale. Nevertheless, in contrast to the present situation in nuclear physics, it must be admitted that there is no conclusive evidence for the need to introduce the idea of cosmical repulsion to account for the mutual recession of the galaxies. Moreover, cosmical repulsion differs from most other forces in physics: unlike gravitational, electrical and nuclear forces it increases with distance, and unlike elastic forces, which do increase with distance, its effect is not cohesive but disruptive.

In Eddington's model cosmical repulsion is initially balanced by world-gravitation, but the equilibrium is unstable and the former tends to predominate over the latter. In Milne's model a different state of affairs prevails. There is initially no ephemeral stationary state. Instead, the relative motions of the constituent 'particles', i.e. galaxies or clusters, are assumed to exist *ab initio*. Unlike Eddington and the orthodox relativistic cosmologists who regarded space itself as expanding and carrying with it the individual galaxies and clusters like straws in a stream, Milne pictured the universe as a cloud of particles spreading out equally in all directions into a vacuum from initial coincidence at a point-like source. In accordance with the cosmological principle, each 'particle' is assumed to be at a centre of symmetry all the time. Consequently, the total world-gravitational force acting on it is zero, since there is no preferred direction in which this force could act. It follows that the particle can continue to move uniformly, just as if no gravitational forces whatsoever were acting on it. This argument was presented rigorously by Milne, but the essential conclusion was that the initial rate of expansion of the model could be maintained undiminished for an indefinite time despite the gravitational interactions of its constituent parts. Instead of invoking a peculiar *force* of cosmical repulsion to make expansion possible, all that was required was the cosmological principle plus the appropriate initial relative *velocities*.

Milne deduced[1] for his uniformly expanding model a simple formula relating epoch t, average density ρ at epoch t, and G, the

[1] With the aid of the basic hypotheses of Kinematic Relativity. (It should be emphasized that these were additional hypotheses to the postulate of uniformity of recessional motion.)

constant of gravitation. Owing to the uniformity of expansion of his model and the three-dimensional nature of space, ρ diminishes as the inverse cube of the epoch. Consequently, his formula

$$\frac{4\pi}{3}G\rho t^2 = 1, \tag{8}$$

implies that in his model G cannot be a true constant but must increase proportionally with t. Substituting the empirically determined values of G and t (in this model t is equal to the reciprocal of the constant of proportionality occurring in Hubble's velocity-distance law), the corresponding value of ρ is found to be about 2×10^{-29} grammes per cubic centimetre according to Sandage's new distance-scale (assuming the *rough* value of 13·5 thousand million years for t).

As regards the gravitational properties of the steady-state model, Bondi and Gold showed in their original paper in 1948 that, if mutual recession were to be compatible with the Perfect Cosmological Principle, then cosmical space-time must be the same as in the empty de Sitter universe. They did not prove, however, that this necessary condition was sufficient, i.e. that continual creation and the Perfect Cosmological Principle would automatically produce the necessary recessional motion. In other words, they did not examine the conditions under which their model would be dynamically possible. Shortly afterwards Hoyle produced an elegant solution to this problem. Whereas Bondi and Gold avoided any appeal to General Relativity, Hoyle showed how Einstein's field equations could be extended by incorporating special terms associated with the incoming matter. He proved that a world-model satisfying the Perfect Cosmological Principle and governed by these equations would have the de Sitter space-time metric. In this way, since the creation terms would be negligible in the usual problems of local gravitation, the steady-state world-model could be reconciled with Einstein's theory of gravitation, although no proof was given that the former would itself automatically give rise to the latter. Hoyle's point of view was subsequently adopted by McCrea who related continual creation of new matter to so-called negative stress.

Hoyle obtained a formula similar to Milne's (equation [8] above), relating the local average density ρ, the reciprocal T of Hubble's constant a, and the constant of gravitation G, viz.

$$\frac{4\pi}{3}G\rho T^2 = \tfrac{1}{2}.\tag{9}$$

In Hoyle's theory G, ρ and T are all true constants, whereas in Milne's they all vary with lapse of time. (With Sandage's distance-scale, the present value of ρ is about 10^{-22} grammes per cubic centimetre.) It is an interesting fact that formula (9) also holds in the Einstein-de Sitter model, but in that case only G is a true constant. The corresponding formula in the Eddington model is

$$\frac{4\pi}{3}G\rho T^2 = \frac{1}{q^3-3q+2},\tag{10}$$

where q is the ratio of the present value of the radius of the universe to its initial value.[1] In this case G is a true constant, but ρ, T and q change with lapse of time.

There is a peculiar difficulty associated with gravitational attraction in the steady-state model. It has been specifically stated by Bondi that, although there may be small variations, 'the creation rate per unit volume per unit time cannot vary widely from place

---

[1] It will be noted that formula (10) agrees with formula (9) when $q = \sqrt{3}$. Since the radius of the empty de Sitter universe is equal to $\sqrt{3}$ times the radius of the static Einstein universe with the same cosmical constant, it follows that formula (9) for the Einstein-de Sitter model applies also to the expanding Einstein-Eddington universe when it has the same size as the corresponding empty de Sitter model.

Incidentally, if Sandage's revision of the distance-scale is accepted and Eddington's theoretical value of R (the initial radius of his world-model) is retained, the present value of q would be only about 1·2. (This value is easily obtained by making his calculated rate of recession of the nebulae, as given by the formula on p. 128, agree with the observed rate.) But from formula (10) it would then follow that the present value of ρ, the local density of matter in the universe, would be of the order of 10^{-27} grammes per cubic centimetre. This value would seem to be excessively high—more than a thousand times that based on observational data, although this latter estimate makes no allowance for any diffuse intergalactic dark matter. It is therefore possible that the magnitude of the discrepancy may ultimately be generally accepted as a decisive reason for rejecting Eddington's theory—or, at least, for modifying it drastically.

to place'. Let us consider what happens to an old cluster of galaxies which will have acquired in and around it an exceedingly powerful local gravitational field through the continual creation of new matter over a long period of time. This field would more than counterbalance the tendency to recession in its immediate neighbourhood (as already mentioned, there is no evidence of mutual recession within the local group of galaxies). Such a cluster would tend to become ever vaster in extent without limit. Since the theory presupposes that all regions of the universe are equivalent, this situation would occur statistically everywhere. Moreover, as it is a fundamental assumption of the theory that there is no evolution of the *universe* (only of individual stars and galaxies), what will happen in the future must already have occurred in the past. Hence, it would seem that there could be no expansion anywhere at any time. For, if it is maintained that clusters of indefinitely large mass occur only outside the region which we can observe, then it would follow that not all regions of the universe are equivalent and that our own region would in fact change with lapse of time as our local group becomes more massive.

McCrea has recently suggested that a possible resolution of this paradox can be found in the application by Sciama, in 1955, of the steady-state theory to the problem of the generation of galaxies and clusters. By its nature, the steady-state theory, unlike evolutionary theories of the universe, cannot pose the problem of an original formation of galaxies, but only of the self-perpetuation of a system of galaxies such as we observe at present. In general, a galaxy will be in motion relative to the intergalactic gas, i.e. will have 'proper motion' in addition to its cosmical recession from other regions of the universe. Sciama argues that the gas that falls towards the galaxy as it passes will tend to form a wake behind it. This wake material will tend to condense under its own gravitation into a second galaxy. In certain circumstances this will ultimately break away from the first galaxy and the process will begin all over again with each separately. If, however, the two remain together, there will be a tendency for the same process to generate a cluster of galaxies. The crucial point in Sciama's theory is that this cluster will *not* grow indefinitely, for in the course of time some galaxies will tend to acquire velocities of escape and thus be lost to the cluster.

Whether this mechanism provides an adequate resolution of the paradox of indefinite growth, we cannot say. For, as McCrea has pointed out, Sciama's theory cannot yet be regarded as established. Until it has been developed in mathematical detail the prudent course will be to suspend judgment on its power to resolve the accretion paradox of the steady-state theory.

Moreover, even if it proves possible to resolve the paradox of indefinitely massive galaxies, the steady-state theory will still have to face the problem of infinitely old galaxies. For, without some additional hypothesis concerning the spontaneous *disappearance* of matter—the counterpart of spontaneous creation—as suggested by Kapp, it follows that an infinite number of infinitely old burnt-out galaxies must necessarily exist. Since our own cluster is not burnt-out and other clusters as they stream away from us are only observable for the earlier part of their histories, no such clusters can be expected within the observable region. But they must exist somewhere, and hence it follows that our region cannot be typical of every region in the universe. Stricly speaking, this is contrary to the Perfect Cosmological Principle on which the theory is based, and a more careful formulation of the fundamental hypotheses is therefore an urgent logical requirement.

The most direct observational test of the steady-state theory would be to investigate intergalactic space and determine the properties and distribution of diffuse matter in the vast regions. For, according to equation (9), the mean density of matter in the steady-state universe is about 10^{-29} grammes per cubic centimetre (on Sandage's new scale). The amount of matter in the form of galaxies is estimated by observational astronomers to be not much more than one per cent. of this. Consequently, it would follow that more than ninety per cent. of all matter must be intergalactic if the steady-state theory is valid. Even if this percentage has to be reduced somewhat, it seems clear that the theory must imply a preponderance of intergalactic matter more or less uniformly distributed in space. This matter will be mainly neutral and ionized hydrogen. The 21-centimetre line of neutral hydrogen has, however, not yet been detected in intergalactic space. This is not surprising, for, owing to the Doppler effect associated with cosmical recession, this radiation would not give rise to a concentrated spectral line but to a band extending on the long-wave side of 21 centimetres. At present it is thought that it would be too weak to be observed, but developments in radio-astronomy in the next few years may enable us to test directly whether hydrogen does exist in the required quantity in intergalactic space. Moreover, it may be possible to decide whether space-reddening of galaxies (similar to that of stars in the Milky Way) can provide a quantitative optical criterion for internebular matter.

Direct evidence for existence of some matter between the nebulae has been obtained by Zwicky in his observations of the Coma cluster with the aid of the 48-inch Schmidt telescope. With its re-markably wide angle of vision this is the most efficient optical instru-ment for discovering such diffuse matter, although the 200-inch reflector is more suited for studying its detailed structure. In the Coma cluster Zwicky claims to have found evidence for the existence not only of dark matter but also of luminous internebular gas of low surface brightness. However, these observations, important as they are, tell us nothing concerning the existence and distribution of matter in space outside the great clusters. According to Hubble, this space is remarkably transparent, but the possibility that it contains diffuse matter of very low density cannot be excluded on purely visual grounds.

Perhaps the decisive observational criterion for deciding between evolutionary and steady-state theories of the universe will ultimately be found in observations bearing on the evolution of galaxies. For example, if astronomers came to the conclusion that all elliptical galaxies observed are about the same age—perhaps 6,000 million years old—this would be a very powerful argument against the steady-state theory. For, according to that theory, we should observe all forms of galaxies in every stage of evolution up to the oldest observable. The way out of the *impasse* in which theoretical cosmologists now find themselves may therefore be found in further detailed study of the structure and characteristics of individual nebulae.

7

THE STRUCTURE OF GALAXIES

OBSERVATION has so far failed to reveal any boundary of the system of nebulae, outside which there could exist similar systems. At present we have every reason for believing that the realm of the nebulae forms the ultimate background of the physical universe. Thus, the nebulae themselves may be regarded as the individual bricks out of which the universe is constructed. So far we have concentrated attention mainly on the architecture of the building formed by these bricks. We will now consider some of the general characteristics and peculiarities of the bricks themselves.

Of the thousand million or more nebulae at present accessible to observation the vast majority can at best be recorded on the photographic plate as mere specks, barely distinguishable from the images of faint stars. A large number of nebulae appear somewhat brighter, but their images are still too small and faint for any details to be observed other than their elongation and the rate at which the brightness fades from the centre towards the edge of the image. Consequently, our knowledge of the structure of individual galaxies is mainly based on a few hundred exceptionally bright nebulae.

These were arranged by Hubble in groups according to their characteristic features, and most of these groups were found to form an ordered sequence which appears to be produced by the continuous variation of a fundamental pattern. Most of the brightest galaxies are called 'regular', since they appear to be rotating more or less symmetrically about central condensations. The others are called 'irregular', because they lack this feature. The regular nebulae fall naturally into two main groups, called 'elliptical' and 'spiral' respectively. When Hubble made his classification of galaxies more than a quarter of a century ago he estimated that about twenty per cent. were elliptical and about seventy-five per cent. spiral, but it is now thought that there are more ellipticals than spirals. According to Baade, of the eighteen galaxies nearest to us ten are ellipticals, but we are not sure whether this proportion is typical.

Elliptical nebulae range from globular objects through ellipsoidal figures to a limiting elongated form with a ratio of axes of about three to one (*see* Plate IV). They are generally free from dust, although small patches of obscuring matter can occasionally be detected against the luminous background. The two main features which have been used for further classification are the shapes of the images and the luminosity gradients, or rates at which the apparent brightness falls off from the centre towards the edge. The former is the simpler criterion to adopt as the shapes of the images and of the contours of equal luminosity can be rapidly determined. These shapes, however, are not true shapes, for they refer to the two-dimensional projected images on the photographic plate and not to the actual three-dimensional nebulae. Thus a circular image may refer to a highly elongated nebula viewed in the direction of its axis of rotation and not necessarily to a spherical nebula. If we assume that the orientation of these axes is distributed at random, we can analyse the shapes of the projected images statistically, and thereby discover the relative abundance of the true forms. It appears that these range from the globular to the lenticular, the latter being the more numerous.

There are two distinct types of spiral nebulae, normal and barred. In general, there are two spiral arms. In the normal spiral they emerge smoothly from opposite regions on the edge of a central condensation which resembles a lenticular nebula. In the barred spiral the two arms emerge abruptly from the opposite ends of a bar of nebulosity stretching right across the central condensation. There appear to be at least twice as many normal spirals as barred spirals. We find that both types of spiral, as well as other types of galaxy can co-exist in the same region of space (*see* Plate V).

The normal spirals can be arranged in a definite sequence. Those at one end of the sequence exhibit a bright central core, the spiral arms being closely coiled. Progressing along the sequence, the arms increase at the expense of the central region and appear to unwind. At the end of the sequence the nucleus is relatively insignificant and the arms are widely open. Peripheral bands of obscuring material are frequently observed in normal spirals, particularly in those seen edge-on (*see* Plate VI).

The barred spirals can also be arranged in a sequence beginning with a shape similar to the Greek letter θ. As the sequence progresses the ring appears to break away from the bar at opposite ends so as to form a crude S, and the spiral arms gradually develop from the free ends. As in the development of the normal spiral, the arms grow at the expense of the central region, unwinding until finally a fully opened S-shape is observed.

The complete sequence of regular types of galaxy can be represented by a Y-shaped diagram. The stem is formed by the elliptical nebulae, with the globular systems at the base and the most elongated systems just below the fork. The two arms are formed by the normal and barred spirals respectively. Between the arms a few spirals of mixed type occur. The transition from the stem to the arm of barred spirals appears to be more or less continuous, but when Hubble originally made his classification there seemed to be a discontinuity between the stem and the arm of normal spirals. However, in later years he introduced a new class of galaxies, designated by the symbol SO, situated in the diagram at the point of junction of the arms and stem of the Y.

Until about fifteen years ago, elliptical nebulae and the cores, but not the arms, of spiral nebulae, appeared to be so concentrated that even with the 100-inch telescope it was not considered possible to resolve them into stars. It was therefore a major triumph of photographic skill when in the autumn of 1944 Baade succeeded in resolving two of the nearest ellipticals and the central region of the great spiral in Andromeda. The outstanding significance of this feat lay, however, in the explanation of its difficulty. Baade pointed out that the former purely nebulous appearance of these objects was due to the abnormally low luminosity of their brightest constituent stars compared with the brightest stars in the arms of spirals. Whereas the brightest stars in the spiral arms are blue super-giants, the brightest stars in the hitherto unresolved galaxies and parts of galaxies are red. Their absolute luminosities are about five magnitudes (roughly 100 times) fainter than those of the brightest stars in the spiral arms. Baade suggested that we must henceforth recognize the existence of two types of stellar population in the nebulae. *Population I,* exemplified by stars in the Sun's neighbourhood, is characterized by the most luminous stars with high surface temperatures (spectral types O and B) and open star-clusters. *Population II* is characterized by RR Lyrae variables and stars such as are found in globular clusters. Whereas in the central regions of spiral nebulae, in elliptical nebulae and in globular clusters only stars of Population II are found, both populations co-exist in the arms of open spirals, Population I predominating (*see* Plate VII). The resolvable irregular galaxies are also Population I systems, although their attendant globular clusters are Population II systems containing many RR Lyrae variables.

Of the irregular galaxies the best known are our two nearest neighbours, the famous Magellanic Clouds. They were first discovered by the Portuguese navigators of the fifteenth century when approaching the Cape of Good Hope, and were first described by a companion of Magellan on his voyage of circumnavigation. They are believed to be about 150,000 light-years away. Both clouds contain large quantities of diffuse matter. The larger cloud is slightly nearer. It is particularly rich in super-giant stars, one of which, S Doradus, is one of the most luminous stars known in the whole visible universe. It is a variable star of a peculiar type, its average brightness being half a million times that of the Sun. It may be a double star of two equal components. In recent years the Magellanic Clouds have been extensively studied at the Mount Stromlo Observatory in Australia, notably by de Vaucouleurs who claims that they are much more extensive than used to be thought (he assigns to them diameters of roughly 50,000 and 20,000 light-years respectively). Moreover, in place of the long accepted view that the Clouds are irregular galaxies with no organized structure, de Vaucouleurs claims that the Large Cloud is a one-armed spiral (most spirals have two arms) of barred type. He argues that the spiral structure of the Small Cloud is more difficult to detect because we see it partly edge on. On the other hand, Lindsay finds no evidence of spiral structure in this system. He thinks it is an irregular galaxy distorted by the tidal action of the Large Cloud.

The Magellanic Clouds belong to a typical small cluster of nebulae forming the so-called *Local Group*, of which our own Galaxy is a member. It includes all galaxies within approximately

2 million light-years from the Sun, and contains about twenty members. According to Baade,[1] we have to travel some 8 million light-years outside this cluster before we reach the next spiral nebula. The Local Group contains two triple systems of nebulae: our own Galaxy and the Magellanic Clouds form one, and the great nebula in Andromeda M31 is a member of another set of three. The Andromeda nebula is visible to the naked eye on clear moonless nights in autumn and winter as an elongated cloud about half the size of the full moon. It lies about twenty-one degrees from the Milky Way circle to the South. The nebula is a typical normal spiral with a relatively large nuclear region, which is the part visible to the unaided eye, and fainter arms. Its distance is somewhat uncertain, but the latest estimate puts it at about 1,600,000 light-years. Its absolute magnitude is approximately −20.

The appearance of the Andromeda nebula varies considerably with the method of viewing. If the elliptical form of the image is due to foreshortening owing to tilt, it is probable that we are viewing the system nearly edge on. Even with the aid of a telescope the size of the nebula to the eye is much smaller than is revealed in good photographs. In the best photographs with the most powerful telescopes it covers a surface area of the sky equal to about seven times that of the Moon, and its length and width are roughly 80,000 and 20,000 light-years respectively. Using the microdensitometer, a sensitive electrical apparatus for measuring photographs, it appears to be much larger still, the nucleus being surrounded by an extensive haze of stars. Indeed, the area of the sky which we now know to be covered by the nebula is equal to not less than seventy full moons. The major and minor axes of this extended image are roughly equal, and we conclude that the outer part of the galaxy is more or less spherical. The whole system looks like a flat wheel with a conspicuous hub, surrounded by a large and spheroidal haze composed of comparatively faint stars.

How the appearance of M31 depends on the method of viewing is shown most strikingly when photographs with different types of plate are compared with each other. On normal blue-sensitive plates the arms stand out clearly, but Baade and Mayall have shown that they are comparatively inconspicuous on photographs made

[1] Before the announcement of Sandage's revision of the distance-scale.

with yellow-sensitive emulsions and in the infra-red. They are again distinctly marked on red-sensitive plates with filters which allow the passage of light due to the Hα line in the spectrum of hydrogen. Careful study of the photographs taken with the 100-inch Mount Wilson and the 200-inch Mount Palomar telescopes show that the best indicators of the spiral arms are blue super-giant O and B stars, patches of hydrogen Hα emission and cosmic dust. (Although long period Cepheid variables are associated with the arms, they also occur between the arms and seem to be considerably more bunched than the other spiral features.) The cosmic dust appears to be localized mainly in the spiral arms and to be most dense along the inner edges. Baade has made the significant discovery that the association of dust and highly luminous blue stars in general marks the beginning of a spiral arm close to the nucleus.

Four spiral arms can be traced on the north side of the Andromeda nebula, five on the south side, and two can be detected well inside the central region. The arms are comparatively narrow, their average width being roughly 2,500 light-years. The distance between neighbouring arms is of the order of 10,000 light-years. Frequently, however, short branches are found to protrude from the main arms. Photometric studies show that, although the arms appear conspicuous on the photographs and are dominated by very bright blue stars, they actually contribute less than one-fifth to the total light emitted. Comparison of photographs of the Andromeda nebula taken in blue and red light also reveals the surprising feature that Population II stars which are prominent in the nucleus are also present a long way out, beyond the spiral structure. According to Baade, these stars form a disc in which the spiral arms are embedded. Population II stars greatly outnumber those of Population I, and he estimates that they probably account for at least ninety-eight per cent. of the total mass of this galaxy.

In many respects the Andromeda nebula is believed to be basically similar to the Milky Way. For example, it is surrounded by at least 300 globular clusters. Also, like our own system, it contains novae (stars which suddenly increase many thousands of times in brightness and then slowly fade). Indeed, the first star identified in an extragalactic nebula was such a new star which was first seen in August 1885, in the central region of M31, and soon attained a luminosity of about ten per cent. of that of the whole nebula. In 1917 two other novae were detected in photographs of the same galaxy. These, however, were thousands of times fainter than the object seen over thirty years before. When Hubble succeeded seven years later in identifying Cepheid variables in M31 and finally established that this system was external to, and comparable with, the Milky Way, it was clear that the 1917 objects were similar to the novae which occur at an average observed rate of about two per year in the Milky Way, whereas the 1885 star was a very much rarer and far more spectacular phenomenon of a totally different type, called *supernova*. We now believe that at least three supernovae have been observed in the Milky Way: the bright star seen by the Chinese in 1054, Tycho Brahe's star of 1572 and Kepler's star of 1604. As already mentioned in Chapter 2, one of the pleasing consequences of Baade's revision of the distance-scale was to bring the average absolute magnitude at maximum brightness for ordinary novae in M31 into line with that for similar stars in the Milky Way.

Like the Milky Way, the Andromeda nebula has two satellite stellar systems, both of which, however, are of elliptical type. The brighter and closer, known as M32, is a highly concentrated galaxy which can be resolved into stars similar to those in the core of M31. The other, known as NGC205, has a nucleus which is considerably fainter than that of M32.

Of the other members of the Local Group, the two nearest to the Milky Way (apart from the Magellanic Clouds) are the curious Fornax and Sculptor galaxies which were discovered in 1938. The Sculptor galaxy appears to be the larger of the two, the respective diameters being about 10,000 and 6,000 light-years. Neither of them fits strictly into any of the three categories of nebulae. They differ from spirals in their lack of structural detail and from ellipticals in their openness and transparency. They differ too from the Magellanic Clouds and other irregular galaxies in being markedly symmetrical. Moreover, they contain no super-giant stars, open clusters or bright gaseous nebulosities.

The remaining members of the Local Group, with one exception, are comparatively minor systems of low absolute luminosity and are either ellipticals or irregulars of the Magellanic type. If these galaxies were 100 million light-years away, our best photographs would probably fail to reveal them. It is therefore reasonable to conclude that there are probably many more comparatively small and faint galaxies in the depths of space than are revealed by our large-scale surveys.

The most distant member of the Local Group is a beautiful open spiral known as the Triangulum Galaxy or M33. Its distance is a little greater than that of the Andromeda nebula, very roughly 1,700 thousand light-years. They are in the same region of the sky, being about 400,000 light-years apart. M33 is much smaller than M31. It has a major diameter of about 50,000 light-years.

Once we pass outside the Local Group, reliable data for the determination of the distances and absolute magnitudes of individual galaxies become increasingly scanty. The beautiful spiral M81 (*see* Plate I) has been studied by Sandage. His estimates of its distance and magnitude are based on the study of one classical Cepheid, several blue irregular variables and twenty novae. It appears that this galaxy is comparable in intrinsic luminosity with the Andromeda nebula.

The estimation of nebular masses like that of all other astronomical bodies and systems depends on Newton's theory of gravitation. Using this theory we can calculate the mass of the Sun, provided the distance of any planet from the Sun and its period of revolution are known. We can also estimate the masses of double stars rotating about each other. The calculation of rotating nebular masses is more difficult.

The gravitational control of the stars in a typical spiral nebula differs from that of the Solar system where nearly all the mass is concentrated in the central Sun and the controlling force therefore varies inversely as the square of the distance from the centre. It differs also from the gravitational field of a continuous discoidal system rotating as a cartwheel. Spectrographic studies indicate that the rotational motion of the outer parts is such that the actual gravitational field probably lies between these two extremes. Hubble originally estimated that the mass of the Andromeda nebula was 3,500 million times that of the Sun, but we now know that he was observing only the central region. The cores of nebulae are usually found to rotate like cartwheels, the speed of rotation at any point being proportional to the distance from the centre. In the outer regions the speed of rotation decreases as we recede from the centre. Towards the rim of M33 the rotation period is about 200 million years and its total mass is about 5,000 million times that of the Sun. On the other hand, the latest estimate for the mass of M31 is about 300,000 million times the Sun's mass. (The respective absolute luminosities of M33 and M31 are 1·4 and 9 thousand million times that of the Sun.) As the mass of the Milky Way is only about 100,000 million times that of the Sun, it now appears that we do *not* inhabit the largest of all known galaxies and that ours is only the second in size of those forming the Local Group.

Another method of estimating the mass of a typical nebula is to consider the individual motions of the members of a cluster of nebulae and calculate the gravitational pull which must be holding the cluster together so that it remains a permanent structure. We can then calculate the mass of the whole cluster and hence deduce the average mass of the nebulae of which it is composed. This method was first applied in 1936 to thirty-two galaxies forming the Virgo cluster, the nearest cluster beyond the Local Group, and yielded an average mass of the order of 200,000 million times that of the Sun. Taking account of Baade's revision of the extragalactic distance-scale, a more recent investigation of the same cluster led to an average mass four times as great. A similar result has been obtained for the average mass of a galaxy in the more remote Coma cluster—about 400,000 million times that of the Sun. These calculations depend, however, on the hypothesis that the clusters concerned have attained a steady state, but the time required for a cluster to attain such a state is enormous; in the case of the Coma cluster it is at least 100,000 million years, i.e. roughly ten times the period during which the universe could have been expanding uniformly.

Nebular masses can also be estimated by studying the relative velocities of double galaxies. This method indicates that there may be a fairly sharp division between giant galaxies of average mass about $1·5 \times 10^{11}$ that of the Sun and dwarf galaxies of about 5×10^9 that of the Sun. Schwarzschild has distinguished between ellipticals and spirals in double galaxies and claims that the average mass of ellipticals in such systems is about 7×10^{10} that of the Sun. From his study of the internal motions of the Magellanic Clouds de

Vaucouleurs argues that, despite his claim that their spatial dimensions are not much less than those of the Milky Way, their respective masses are only about 5×10^9 and $1 \cdot 5 \times 10^9$ that of the Sun.

Despite the fact that for many years astronomers have accepted the theory that the great nebulae are similar structures to the Milky Way, until recently it seemed that our own Galaxy was larger than any other stellar system. Baade's revised estimate of the distance of the Andromeda nebula led, however, to the conclusion that this galaxy is larger than our own, although the overwhelming majority of galaxies are smaller. Shapley's estimate in 1918 of the dimensions of our Galaxy was strictly speaking an estimate of the dimensions of the enveloping system of globular clusters. This is completely unaffected by Baade's revision of the distance-scale because the distances of these clusters were obtained from the study of RR Lyrae variables and not of classical Cepheids. There is no doubt that the flattened wheel-like distribution of stars which constitutes the main body of the Milky Way represents the equatorial plane of the system of globular clusters, but the precise limits of this disc are by no means clearly defined. Instead of there being a definite rim, the stars gradually peter out at great distances from the centre. In principle, we could define the edge of a galaxy as the region where the star-density in space falls below a definite fraction, e.g. one-thousandth, of the density at the centre. Unfortunately, this does not provide a practical criterion. Instead, one has to make standard exposures with the same telescope and compare the images by a standard procedure. This method is satisfactory for the comparison of the extragalactic nebulae with each other, but does not help in comparing them with the Milky Way. Indeed, the star-density in the region which we are disposed to regard as the outer rim of the Milky Way may be less than in the outermost detectable rim of the Andromeda nebula. Thus we may tend to exaggerate the dimensions of the former and underestimate those of the latter.

The main difficulty in investigating the Milky Way is due to the fact that we are located in just about the worst possible place for observation. Not only are we at the outskirts of the Galaxy, but we are also in such a dusty region that we cannot see very far in any direction in the Galactic plane. As Bok has remarked, 'It is as though we were attempting, on a foggy day, to study the plan of a large city

from the roof of a not-too-high building somewhere in the suburbs.'
Because the layer of Galactic dust swells out to its greatest thickness in the direction of the centre, surveys have been made in the
opposite direction, away from this hub. In this direction also there
is a considerable amount of light-absorbing dust, and we suspect
that our Galaxy is surrounded by a ring of obscuration such as we
observe in so many of the external galaxies (*see* Plate VI).

Nevertheless there are in this direction some comparatively
transparent regions, through which we can faintly discern systems
in outer space. It is in these regions that we can best seek to determine the confines of our own system, particularly by means of
Cepheid variables. Of course, the distances of such stars cannot be
determined accurately if we are unable to assess the amount of light
absorption by the dust in intervening space. We can, however,
estimate this effect by counting the number of external galaxies
shown on long exposure plates in the same direction. The effects of
non-uniformity of distribution of the nebulae can only be circum-
vented by dealing with large areas involving many variable stars
and tens of thousands of galaxies, thereby smoothing out irregularities and consequent errors.

According to our present knowledge, the distance of the anti-
centre, or rim, of the Milky Way in the opposite direction to the
centre, is at least 15,000 light-years, but individual stars have been
found at twice this distance. The distance of the centre, which is
located in the direction of the great star cloud in Sagittarius, has
been estimated by Baade to be about 27,000 light-years (8,200
parsecs), but according to Thackeray the most probable value is
now (January 1958) considered to be about 30,000 light-years. It
had been thought that the centre was hidden from us by a great dark
cloud of obscuring matter, but in 1946 Baade suggested that parts of
the Sagittarius cloud actually belong to the central nucleus.[1] Thus
the effective diameter of the main plane of the Milky Way is nearly
100,000 light-years. Although we believe that the star-density decreases rapidly at this limit, there are scattered stars, including
short-period Cepheids, extending to perhaps 15,000 light-years
outside the boundary.

Similarly, the thickness of the Milky Way is not sharply defined.

[1] The main diameter of this nucleus may be 5,000 light-years or more

The stellar density decreases to one-tenth of that in the neighbour-hood of the Sun at about 1,500 light-years from the main plane, so that the vast majority of the stars lie in a layer, the thickness of which in the region of the Sun is some 3,000 light-years. This layer increases considerably in thickness and density towards the Galactic centre. The thickness of the spheroidal hub is 15,000 or more light-years. Its principal diameter (in the central plane) is roughly 40,000 light-years, the Sun being probably about 10,000 light-years beyond its outer edge. Oort has estimated that the average density in the hub is about twice that in the vicinity of the Sun. Inside the hub there may be a central core of still higher density. Surrounding the whole system there are scattered stars and globular clusters defining a more or less spherical region of diameter about 130,000 light-years.

Our Galaxy contains not only stars but also many luminous and dark clouds. Until the present century, however, it was not realized that, as in the case of spirals which we see edge on, there is a large quantity of far more diffuse and rarified obscuring matter in and near the main plane of the Milky Way. We now believe that in our region of the Galaxy at least one-third and perhaps one-half of matter exists in this form.[1] According to the latest estimates, most of it is gas (predominantly hydrogen), but about one per cent. consists of dust, i.e. tiny solid pellets.

The discovery of interstellar gas dates from an important obser-vation in 1904 by the German astonomer Hartmann. While study-ing the light emanating from the star Delta Orionis he found that in its spectrum one of the lines due to ionized calcium was peculiar. The other lines were broad and fuzzy, indicating that Delta Orionis actually consisted of two stars revolving around each other. The peculiar line of calcium, on the other hand, was sharp and distinct. Later work suggested that this line was due to calcium vapour lying between the star and ourselves.

The first systematic study of the subject was made by Plaskett. In 1924 he showed conclusively that the positions of certain lines of calcium and sodium in the spectra of a number of stars differed from their normal positions in such a way that it was clear that they

---

[1] There is, however, much less diffuse matter in the central regions of the Milky Way.

could not arise in the atmospheres of these stars. He concluded that they must be produced by ionized calcium and neutral sodium in interstellar space. Subsequent theoretical investigations showed that calcium and sodium were the only reasonably abundant elements which could yield spectral lines observable under the conditions of stimulation prevailing in interstellar space.[1] Eddington calculated that the density of interstellar matter (in our part of the Galaxy) was of the order of 10^{-24} grammes per cubic centimetre, which is about one atom per cubic centimetre if, as in the stars, most of the atoms are hydrogen. As he remarked: 'One atom per cubic centimetre does not amount to much. A portion of the cosmic cloud as large as the earth could, if compressed, be packed in a suitcase and easily carried with one hand.'

In 1930 Plaskett and Pearce showed that the intensity of the interstellar lines is directly proportional to the distance of the stars in whose spectra they are observed, indicating that interstellar matter is distributed more or less uniformly throughout the intervening space, a result which has been considerably modified in recent years as individual clouds have come to be distinguished from the general tenuous medium. They concluded that diffuse matter must extend to at least 6,000 light-years from the Sun and probably to the confines of the system. They established, moreover, that the interstellar gas shares in the Galactic rotation, as it is nearly stationary with respect to the frame of reference determined by the average motion of the stars.

The reason why interstellar matter was not found earlier is because only certain stars show the effect discovered by Hartmann. First, the stars must be at least 1,000 light-years distant, so that the thickness of cloud in the intervening space is sufficient to produce a detectable effect. At the same time the star must be sufficiently bright to enable us to study its spectrum adequately. Consequently, the star must have an extremely high intrinsic brightness. Moreover, the star must not show in its own spectrum the calcium and sodium lines which appear in the spectra of interstellar vapour, for when these lines appear in the spectrum of a star's atmosphere they are usually so strong and broad that they could mask the sharp lines of

[1] Since then, however, other elements and molecules have been detected in interstellar space.

the cosmic cloud. Hence, only comparatively few stars will show the required effect.

Further evidence for the existence of interstellar matter was provided by Trumpler's study of *similar* open Galactic star-clusters. Assuming that they all have the same absolute luminosity, Trumpler found that the diameters of the most distant were nearly twice as large as those of the nearest. As it is most improbable that this is a real effect, he concluded that the distances of the more remote clusters had been overestimated, thus causing him to overestimate their diameters. He attributed this to the effect of interstellar gas in diminishing the apparent brightness. He concluded that the absorbing matter was concentrated towards the Galactic plane in a layer 600 to 1,000 light-years thick.

The cosmic haze is only roughly homogeneous, and there exist regions in which it is much denser than the average. These include vast clouds 100 or more light-years across; in general they are dark and opaque, or at best semi-transparent, but some are faintly luminous. These clouds are most numerous in the Milky Way where they can be seen silhouetted against the background of more distant stars. Clouds of this type predominate in the direction of the Galactic centre. Strömgren has tentatively estimated that they occupy about five per cent. of space near the Galactic plane. He has calculated that their average density is probably more than a hundred times greater than that of the general haze. The average number of clouds encountered by light travelling in the Galactic plane in the neighbourhood of the Sun is perhaps two in a thousand years. Many of these clouds contain small dust particles which scatter, or deflect, the bluer rays, thereby causing many stars to appear redder than normal, just as the light from the Sun appears redder when seen through smoke or fog. This space-reddening of distant stars, particularly the highly luminous O and B stars, has been studied intensively in recent years, notably by Stebbins, and has become one of the most important sources of information concerning interstellar clouds.

We call the whole tenuous medium pervading the Galaxy the *absorbing layer*. Hubble has shown how the existence of the absorbing layer accounts for the observed distribution of extra-galactic nebulae. The average numbers of nebulae per plate are greatest in the regions of the sky farthest from the Milky Way, where obscuration from the absorbing layer is least. Towards the Galactic plane the numbers per plate decrease in a way which suggests that the obscuration is roughly proportional to the length of the light-paths through a uniform layer of obscuration. In comparing the theoretical world-models with the observed distribution of nebulae, the latter must, of course, first be corrected for the effects of this obscuration.

In recent years much work has been done on the analysis of stellar distribution in the Galaxy. For example, as we rise above the Galactic plane, the giant stars thin out much more rapidly than the dwarfs. Also, analysis of available star-counts indicates that in almost every direction the star-density drops with increasing distance from the Sun. This diminution in the direction of the anti-centre was not unexpected, but the initial diminution in the direction of the Galactic centre was more surprising, particularly as there is a marked increase again beyond a distance of some two or three thousand light-years. By analogy with the extragalactic nebulae, it would appear as if our Sun were located in a minor spiral arm or knot of elongated shape. The initial decrease in star-density towards the Galactic centre would then be due to our passing beyond the spiral arm in which the Sun is located, and the subsequent increase in star-density at greater distances to our penetration of the main body of the Galaxy or another arm.

For many years evidence has been accumulating that the Milky Way is in fact a spiral of intermediate type, similar to the great nebula in Andromeda, and that the Sun is situated in a spiral arm. We are surrounded in most directions in the main plane by highly luminous O and B stars, extensive luminous galactic nebulae and cosmical dust, all features associated with spiral arms in extragalactic nebulae. Nevertheless, it is only in the last few years that astronomers have succeeded in beginning to trace the arms of our own system. The first results were obtained by Morgan of the Yerkes Observatory who announced in 1951 that parts of two arms were clearly indicated and that there was possibly a third arm. The first arm, which Morgan called the *Orion Arm*, was traced for about 12,000 light-years from the constellation of Cygnus through Cepheus, Cassiopeia's chair, Perseus and Orion to Monoceros. He suggested that the Great Rift, where the Milky Way seems to divide into two separate branches, marks a part of the dark lane on the inner side of this arm. He estimated that the Orion Arm is about 1,200 light-years wide and that the Sun is situated inside it at between 100 and 200 light-years from the inner edge. There is some evidence that a short spike protrudes from this arm. The second spiral arm, called the *Perseus Arm*, lies outside the Orion arm, i.e. farther from the Galactic centre, and passes the Sun at about 7,000 light-years. The third arm, called the *Sagittarius Arm*, is difficult to detect from observatories in the Northern hemisphere, but has since been charted at the Boyden Station in South Africa. It lies between the Orion Arm and the Galactic centre.

Owing to cosmical dust, optical methods appear to be powerless to extend our knowledge of the spiral structure of the Milky Way to distances beyond 15,000 light-years from the Sun. Fortunately, the discovery by radio-astronomers in the last few years of the 21-centimetre spectral line of neutral hydrogen in interstellar space (as described in Chapter 5) has enabled them to trace out the spiral arms to much greater distances. The Leiden group have succeeded in mapping a section of an arm that stretches from the region of the Sun nearly half-way around our Galaxy to a distance of some 50,000 light-years.

We have seen that the globular clusters form a vast spheroidal super-system surrounding, and nearly concentric with, the highly flattened stellar system. This structure could be explained if the flat system were rotating about an axis, while the globular clusters were not. Study of the radial velocities of globular clusters reveals that they are all tending to move relative to the Sun in a direction which is very nearly at right angles to the direction of the Galactic centre, with speeds ranging from 200 to 250 kilometres per second. This peculiar systematic asymmetry in their motion strongly suggests that the Sun and its neighbours are all turning about the Galactic centre at a rate of more than 200 kilometres per second.

The earliest suggestion that the Galaxy is rotating was made by Sir John Herschel. If the Galaxy rotated like a cartwheel it would be extremely difficult to detect this rotation, because relatively to each other the stars on the average would be stationary. Instead, the type of rotation for which we look is that of Saturn's rings. In a famous memoir, Clerk Maxwell showed a hundred years ago that Saturn's rings would be unstable if they were solid, and that they must consist of a swarm of separate bodies. In a system of particles rotating about a centre of gravitational attraction the innermost particles will rotate more rapidly than the outermost, in order to counteract the stronger gravitational pull towards the centre.

In studying the problem of Galactic rotation we are almost entirely dependent on the determination of velocities in the line of sight, which can be measured spectroscopically by the Doppler effect. Only for the nearest stars can we determine motions transverse to the line of sight, by comparing their positions over a considerable interval of time. On the theory of Galactic rotation stars which are farther from the centre than the Sun will tend, in general, to move more slowly, i.e. relative to the Sun they will lag behind, whereas stars nearer to the centre will race ahead. It is this differential rotation which we must seek in our observations. There should be no average radial velocity in the line of the Sun's motion nor in the line at right angles to this; for stars in the former line will have the velocity of the Sun, and stars in the latter will be moving transversely to the line of sight.

The general differential effect can be visualized most easily by considering stars in a square centred on the Sun and lying in the plane of the Galaxy, two sides being parallel to the direction of the Galactic centre. The stars on the outer edge will move backwards relative to the Sun, while the stars on the inner edge will move forward. Consequently, the square will gradually be distorted into the shape of a diamond, two of its vertices being compressed towards the Sun and two being drawn away from it. Hence along one diagonal the observed radial velocities should be towards the Sun, and along the other they should be away from it. These diagonals should be equally inclined to the lines of zero radial velocity. Moreover, on the average, the radial velocities should increase with increasing distance from the Sun. This effect was first traced by Oort in 1927, and he deduced that the Galaxy was rotating about a centre in the direction of Sagittarius, thus providing an independent check on Shapley's estimation of the direction of the Galactic centre deduced from the direction of the globular clusters.

The theory of Galactic rotation implies that we can no longer regard either the Sun or the mean standard determined by the motion of the stars in our neighbourhood as providing an ultimate standard of rest in the universe. The centre of the Galaxy is a more fundamental standard, although it too can hardly be ultimate when we consider that in all probability the Milky Way has its own proper motion relative to the system of nebulae. The introduction of the Galactic centre as an origin of reference, however, has made us realize that the apparent approach of the Andromeda nebula is partly the reflection of the Sun's high speed of rotation in its direction.

Although Oort's theory of a smoothly rotating Galaxy must be regarded as only a first approximation, the Sun's motion differs only slightly from the average circular motion about the Galactic centre of most Population I stars and interstellar clouds in its neighbourhood. The Sun moves about the centre in a nearly circular ellipse which vibrates slowly through a small angle in the direction perpendicular to the main plane of the Milky Way, two or three of these oscillations occurring in the 200 million years of a complete revolution. Knowing that the Sun's orbit is nearly circular and that most of the matter in the Milky Way is much closer to the centre, it can easily be calculated on the basis of Newton's theory of gravitation, given the period of the Sun's revolution and its distance from the centre, that the total mass of the Milky Way is roughly 100,000 million times that of the Sun. The calculation is similar to that by which the mass of the Andromeda nebula is determined (as mentioned above).

The velocity of revolution of the solar system about the centre of the Milky Way is about 220 kilometres per second. In our neighbourhood there are certain relatively fast-moving Population II stars, notably RR Lyrae variables, with an average speed of about 130 kilometres per second in the direction *opposite* to that of the Sun's motion. Relative to the centre of the Galaxy, however, these so-called 'high-velocity' stars are in fact laggards, moving with speeds of the order of 100 kilometres per second in the same direction as the Sun.[1] Unlike the Sun, these stars are not moving in

[1] It is interesting to note that there are no stars moving in the same direction as the Sun with high velocity. If a star in our region of the Galaxy had a *relative* velocity in this direction of order 100 kilometres per

nearly circular orbits but in elongated ellipses which extend towards the Galactic centre. Although none of the RR Lyrae stars in our neighbourhood ever come nearer than half-way to the centre, some weak-line F stars[1] move in such elongated orbits that they may have come from as close as 5,000 light-years from the centre, and so may be regarded as visitors from the very heart of the Milky Way to our outer region.

Until a few years ago there was much controversy concerning the sense in which spiral nebulae rotate. From observational studies of the internal motions of extragalactic systems Hubble tentatively deduced that the arms trail behind, their convex sides facing the direction of rotation. On the other hand, Lindblad maintained that the concave sides face this direction. Following a detailed theoretical study of the stability of rotating stellar systems, he argued that a disturbance on an equatorial rim which is on the verge of instability would cause spiral arms to be ejected in the sense in which the nebula is rotating. The difficulty in deciding the issue empirically was due to the fact that, if the arms of a spiral are to be clearly seen, the main plane of the nebula must not be inclined at too great an angle to the line of sight. But then it is extremely difficult to decide which is the nearer edge to us. On the other hand, if the spiral is presented edge on so that this particular difficulty does not arise, it is well nigh impossible to observe the spiral structure. Fortunately, as a result of the recent successes in tracing out lengthy segments of the arms of the Milky Way, it has now become clear that the convex sides do in fact face the direction of rotation and that therefore the arms trail behind as our Galaxy rotates. The same feature has also been discovered in the Andromeda nebula and in the spiral NGC253.

These discoveries confirm that differential rotation is a crucial factor influencing spiral structure. For, if a stream of matter is ejected from the central regions of a galaxy, the slower rotational speed of the outer regions would presumably bend the stream back into a curved arm trailing behind as the galaxy continues to spin.

second, it would in fact be moving at more than 300 kilometres per second with respect to the Galactic centre. We believe that such a star would have the velocity of escape and would ultimately cease to be a member of our stellar system. It is therefore not surprising that no such stars have been observed.

[1] These are stars of a particular spectral type.

Nevertheless, the theoretical problem of spiral arms is still far from complete solution and elucidation. The pioneer mathematical researches of Lindblad, Milne and others were mainly confined to the dynamical aspects of the problem, but in recent years it has become increasingly clear that such an approach is far too restrictive. The great discrepancies between nebular masses and luminosities, when measured in terms of the Sun's mass and luminosity, indicate that the vast majority of stars in the universe must be comparatively faint. On the other hand, since spiral arms are dominated by the rare highly luminous blue stars, they appear much more prominent on photographic plates than they otherwise would. Consequently, the appearance of spiral shape would seem to be primarily a luminosity rather than a mass effect.

Moreover, it is becoming abundantly clear that spiral arms must be comparatively transitory phenomena. For not only are the dominant stars in these arms relatively short-lived, existing only for periods of time comparable with, or even less than, the period of one revolution, but since the outer parts revolve more slowly than the inner, it follows that in the course of a few revolutions the arms would become all twined up. In fact, the arms usually show only one or two complete turns. The main problem facing the theoretical student of nebular structure is therefore to account for the origin and continued existence of spiral arms. In the case of the Milky Way, with an average spacing of about 6,000 light-years and an average rate of diminution of rotational velocity with distance from centre of about 3 kilometres per second per thousand light-years, the present arms will rapidly dissolve unless they can be rejuventated by a process not yet understood. Without such a process they cannot be older than 200 million years.

The pioneer theoretical investigators of spiral structure assumed that the forces concerned were inertial and gravitational, but in the last few years evidence has accumulated that other forces may also be involved. In 1949 it was found that the light from some space-reddened stars, i.e. stars that appear to be reddened due to intervening material, is also partially plane-polarized. To produce this effect a preponderance of somewhat elongated particles in interstellar space is required. The fact that polarization is associated with space-reddening indicates that dust particles are concerned and that some mechanism must exist to align these particles in more or less the same direction over vast regions extending up to 100 parsecs or more. The most probable large-scale force which could produce this effect is an interstellar or general galactic magnetic field. Just as iron filings are orientated along the lines of force of a bar magnet, so similar alignment processes are believed to affect cosmical dust. Although there is no general agreement yet concerning the origin of such processes, many astronomers welcome the suggestion that magnetic fields on the required scale may exist. One of the most striking phenomena which seems to support this theory is the beautiful alignment of long wisps of bright and dark nebulosity observed in large tracts of the Milky Way. The Russian astronomer Shajn has calculated for some regions the magnetic fields which could cause such phenomena and finds that their directions agree reasonably well with those derived for the observed polarization effects for stars seen through these filamentary nebulosities.

Whether or not magnetic fields do in fact play an important part in arranging the gas clouds of our own and other galaxies in the familiar spiral patterns, the existence of non-gravitational forces on this scale has been postulated by the Australian radio-astronomers. Their investigations on the distribution of interstellar hydrogen have led them to conclude that the Milky Way is tilted out of its main plane like a hat with a flexible brim—up at one end, and down at the other in the direction of the Magellanic Clouds. They maintain that this tilt exceeds that which could be ascribed to gravitational attraction alone and therefore argue that other forces may be involved. They have traced several arms of the Milky Way in the southern sky (the hemisphere in which the Magellanic Clouds lie) and claim that in the regions between these arms there is more gas than in the corresponding regions observable in the northern sky. They estimate that, whereas only two per cent. of the total mass of the Milky Way[1] consists of interstellar gas, the regional percentage rises at the outer edges to about fifty.[2] In our neighbourhood it is

[1] A similar result has been obtained by van de Hulst for the Andromeda nebula.

[2] A recent investigation of the 21-centimetre radiation in the spirals M51 and M81 indicates that each is imbedded in a halo of hydrogen which extends far beyond the optical limits. In a typical spiral such a halo may be more massive than the relatively concentrated gas associated with the arms.

about fifteen. On the other hand, nearly half the total mass of the Magellanic Clouds appears to be in the form of uncondensed gas and dust.[1] We may, therefore, tentatively conclude that the relative mass of interstellar gas varies from an extremely small fraction in the case of elliptical galaxies to one or two per cent. in large spirals, and perhaps up to about fifty per cent. in 'irregular' systems like the Magellanic Clouds.

Recently, Oort and his colleagues in a study of 21-centimetre radiation from the hub of the Milky Way have found evidence of a spiral arm in the central region which is moving towards us and also swinging around the centre. The speed of approach ranges from about 50 to 200 kilometres per second. The total mass involved is thought to be such that the whole of the disc within two kiloparsecs of the centre would be emptied in fifty million years if there were no replenishment. This may, however, come from the halo of rarefied gas revealed by 21-centimetre observations in the form of a vast corona surrounding the whole Milky Way. The total mass of this halo is not yet known, but it is probably safe to predict that the remarkable phenomenon of an expanding inner spiral arm will have a profound bearing on the problem of spiral structure.

Whatever the ultimate explanation of spiral structure may prove to be, there is now no doubt among astronomers that spiral arms, Population I stars and cosmical gas and dust are all intimately related. As Oort has recently stated, not only does gas play an important part in spiral arms, but it is even probable that gas is the primary constituent and that the stars concentrated in the arms are only a by-product. In his view, which is widely shared at the present time, 'These results suggest that it may be the specific properties of the gas that give rise to the spiral structures. In what way they do is still obscure. One can understand why the gas has a tendency to contract to a flat disc, as it has done in the Galactic System. One can similarly understand that the differential angular rotation will draw out irregularities into spiral or circular bands. But the large-scale structures extending over the whole system remain as yet unexplained.'

----

[1] It may be significant that, although these galaxies have perhaps only a fiftieth of the mass of the Milky Way, their total radio-emission is roughly a third.

8

THE EVOLUTION OF THE UNIVERSE

What did God before He made heaven and earth?
I answer not as one is said to have done merrily,
eluding the pressure of the question, 'He was
preparing hell (saith he) for pryers into mysteries.'

Confessions of St. Augustine, XI, I4.

ACCORDING to Archbishop Ussher, God created the world on
Sunday, 23rd October, 4004 B.C.[1] Recent scientific attempts to date
the remote past are, I am afraid, much less precise. The complexities
of the problem are now more evident than they once were, and there
is not even general agreement among theoretical cosmologists that
the age of the universe is finite. Nevertheless, I believe that, in the
light of present knowledge, two broad conclusions can be drawn:
first, as we shall see, several independent lines of evidence, based on
the analysis of empirical data concerning the origin of various
physical objects, all lead to results of the same order of magnitude;
second, this impressive agreement as regards order of magnitude
sharpens the problem of the temporal origin of the universe so that
we can now ask not merely whether there was such an origin, but
more precisely whether the scale of past time is confined to a few
thousand million years.

Until recent times all estimates of the age of the Earth or the age
of the universe were purely speculative. By a curious coincidence,
just as the first theory of the structure of the world, according to
Thales, concerned water, so the first theory of how to estimate the
range of past time depended on the composition of the seas and
oceans of the world. In the Middle Ages, Dante and others believed
in the unity of all Earthly waters. This concept was queried by the

[1] J. Ussher, *The Annals of the World Deduced from the Origin of Time*,
London, 1658, p. 1.

great Hohenstaufen Emperor Frederick the Second, who was puzzled that sea-water was so salt, while river-water was not. Nearly five hundred years later this distinction suggested to the astronomer Halley a possible method of estimating the age of the world. In a communication to the Royal Society in 1715 he pointed out that the sea had become salt because of the accumulation of saline material swept down by rivers. He regretted that the ancient Greeks had not 'delivered down to us the degree of saltness of the sea, as it was about two thousand years ago', so that the difference between the saltness then and now could be used to estimate the age of the oceans.

Halley's suggestion was revived by Joly about fifty years ago. Assuming that the average annual amount of dissolved sodium removed by rivers from the land had remained constant throughout geological time, he estimated that about 100 million years would be required to provide the oceans with their present amount. It is now realized, however, that this method is much less accurate than Joly imagined. From the most recent investigations, Joly's assumption of past uniformity indicates an age of the order of 250 million years, but it can by no means be safely assumed that the rate of increase in the salinity of the oceans has been uniform. At present the land areas of the world are believed to be much more elevated than has usually been the case in the past, and rivers are much more active in consequence. Only a very rough estimate can be made of the effect of these and other influences, and the most that can be said is that the age of the oceans must be reckoned at least in hundreds, and perhaps in thousands, of millions of years.

Towards the end of the last century an alternative method of calculating the age of the Earth was devised by Lord Kelvin. He pointed out that, as there is a measurable flow of heat through the Earth's crust, indicated by the downward increase of temperature, the Earth must be cooling and hence must have been hotter in the past. He calculated the epoch at which the Earth was molten, finally concluding that this must have been between 20 and 40 million years ago. This estimate for the age of the Earth was in general agreement with his estimate for the age of the Sun. Helmholtz had suggested that the Sun maintains its enormous outpouring of radiation by continually shrinking and thereby releasing energy. If a body falls freely in a gravitational field it acquires kinetic energy, or energy of motion. If this motion is stopped, the energy thus acquired must be transformed in some way. In the case of a shrinking Sun, Helmholtz suggested that the energy acquired as the outer regions fall in towards the centre appears as radiation. Kelvin calculated that the shrinkage of the Sun to its present size could hardly have provided energy for more than about 50 million years of radiation.

Kelvin's calculations gave rise to a violent controversy between geologists and physicists. The geologists maintained that far longer periods of time were required to explain the known sequence of sedimentary strata and also to allow for the evolution of biological species. In particular, James Geikie showed in 1900 that the crustal compression resulting from 100 million years of cooling of the Earth's crust would be confined to a shell which would be far too thin to accommodate the enormous thicknesses of folded rocks involved in the Alps and other great mountain ranges.

The flaw in Kelvin's method was not revealed until the turn of the century. Following the discovery of radium, Lord Rayleigh showed that this radioactive element occurs in common rocks all over the world. Thus the crustal rocks contain an unfailing source of heat of their own. Moreover, it is now known that there is a sufficient supply of radioactive elements in these rocks to make the net loss of heat extremely small, so that age estimates based on the rate of cooling are correspondingly increased. It is now thought that about ninety per cent. of the heat-flow through the rocks is due to radioactivity, and Kelvin's figure of 20 to 40 million years has to be multiplied about a hundredfold.

The decay of radioactive elements, however, has itself provided new and far superior methods for estimating the range of geological time. Early in the present century Rutherford and Soddy discovered that in each deposit of a radioactive element the number of atoms which disintegrate in unit time is proportional to the total number of atoms of the element. The constant of proportionality was found to be independent of pressure, temperature and other physical conditions, and to depend only on the particular element concerned. Thus, the rate of decay of a given element could be used as a scale of time. When uranium and thorium decay they pass through a series of transformations; in particular, at one stage of uranium decay radium occurs. The ultimate stable end-products are helium and lead. By measuring the amount of these stable end-products in a rock containing uranium or thorium we can estimate the age of the rock. In practice more reliable results are obtained from studying the lead than the helium, as the latter is a gas and so more liable to escape. Fortunately, it is possible to distinguish between lead of radioactive origin and lead which is not produced in this way. If a radioactive mineral has not been affected by weathering and other changes, the amount of lead of radioactive origin now present in it depends on the amount of uranium and/or thorium now present and the period which has elapsed since the mineral originally crystallized. Hence, by measuring the amount of radiogenic lead present and comparing it with the amount of uranium and/or thorium, we can calculate the age of the mineral.

In practice this method can be checked by considering separately the three different isotopes, or varieties, of lead of radioactive origin and examining the consistency of our results. For example, the latest calculations agree to within a few per cent. in assigning about 255 million years since the close of the Devonian period, when the highest form of life is believed to have been fish. The Cambrian age, from which the earliest fossils date, probably occurred between 440 and 500 million years ago, while to the oldest mineral so far investigated, uraninite from Manitoba, has been assigned the tremendous age of 1,985 million years. Associated with this mineral are pebbles of still older granites and quartzites which must therefore be more than 2,000 million years old.

In order to determine how much older than this the Earth is likely to be, Holmes devised in 1946 a method depending on the existence of a fourth isotope of lead (Pb^{204}) which is not generated by any naturally radioactive element. While it cannot be assumed that primeval lead consisted solely of this particular isotope, it is reasonable to assume that lead which contains the lowest proportion of the other three isotopes in relation to Pb^{204} is closest in composition to primeval lead. By selecting specimens of lead minerals of known age and isotope composition the separate variations of the radioactive isotopes can be plotted graphically against time. The remarkable result emerged that, despite the uncertainties of the data, a fair proportion of the lines tended to cross at the same point, from which a time-value could be read. In this way, Holmes claimed that the most probable age of the Earth's crust was 3,350 million years, and he argued that this was virtually the age of the Earth itself. Many geologists believe that this time must be regarded as a minimum for the continental masses and that the Earth's crust may have existed in a relatively undifferentiated state prior to the formation of continents. Sir Harold Jeffreys maintains, however, that the time calculated by Holmes is an over-estimate and that, if data from two ores which he rejected had been included, the result would have been less than 2,600 years. Jeffreys argues that the close agreement of the data used by Holmes may be accidental and that the ores rejected may be no less typical than those retained. Other authorities, using the same data, have found, however, that the ratio of the radiogenic isotope Pb^{207} to the non-radiogenic isotope Pb^{204} extrapolates to zero at 5,500 million years ago.

Although the lead-method is preferable to the helium-method for estimating the ages of rocks, the latter method has been applied to determine the ages of meteorites. These are lumps of iron, nickel and other minerals which enter the Earth's atmosphere from outer space and succeed in reaching the Earth's surface before being burnt up by their rapid passage through the air. It is believed that they originate in the solar system. Paneth subjected a number of meteorites to careful analysis and found a considerable variation in their helium content, although the percentage of uranium and thorium was nearly identical in each. Arguing that meteoritic iron has an extremely high helium-retentivity, he concluded that the variation in helium content was due to the variation in age of the meteorites since solidification. The ages assigned by this method and published by Paneth in 1942 showed a wide spread, ranging from a mere 60 million years to 7,600 million years, i.e. about twice Holmes' estimates for the age of the Earth.

In the mid-nineteen-forties many cosmologists were puzzled by the fact that both these lines of enquiry led to ages significantly greater than the reciprocal of Hubble's constant which was at that time believed to be approximately 2,000 million years. Although not all cosmologists regarded the latter as a direct measure of the age of the universe, many interpreted it in that way. It was this paradox which led Bondi, Gold and Hoyle to formulate the steady-state theory of continual creation and thereby to assign an infinite measure to the age of the universe.

In the same year (1948) as this theory was first published, serious doubts were thrown on the validity of Paneth's methods. It was pointed out that cosmic rays which are believed to be far more intense outside the Earth's atmosphere than on the Earth's surface, could give rise to nuclear changes in iron atoms with the frequent release of alpha particles which become helium atoms. Thus in interplanetary space meteorites could accumulate helium as a result of cosmic-ray bombardment. Consequently, all metallic meteorites are likely to be contaminated by helium from cosmic rays, and the 'ages' derived by Paneth on the hypothesis that all the helium in these meteorites was from uranium and thorium are too high. Of the helium due to cosmic-ray bombardment it has been estimated that nearly one-third will be the isotope helium-3, whereas that produced by the decay of uranium and thorium will be helium-4. It is, therefore, possible to subtract the helium-3 and the associated helium-4 (due to cosmic-ray action) and to regard the remaining helium in a meteorite as due to uranium and thorium. It has been found that for meteorites of moderate helium content, for which the separation of the two types of helium is most accurate, the maximum radiogenic 'ages' do not exceed 250 million years. This may be regarded as the time which has elapsed since they solidified. Although it is now evident that the problem of dating meteorites is extremely complex,[1] we can assert with reasonable confidence that the upper age-limit is not likely to be much greater than 1,000 million years. It would seem that they were produced by catastrophes which occurred long after the formation of the solar system.

An important method of using data concerning radioactivity to estimate an upper limit to the age of matter in the Earth's crust depends on the fact that, in general, isotopes of odd atomic weight are less abundant than those of even atomic weight. At the present time the ratio of uranium-235 to uranium-238 is about 1 to 139. The half-period (i.e. the time during which fifty per cent. of any given amount spontaneously decays) is about 700 million years for

[1] An additional complication which may yet have to be taken into account is the imperfect helium-retentivity of meteorites. It seems most unlikely that no helium is lost in the course of many millions of years.

the former and about 4,500 million years for the latter. It can be calculated that both isotopes would have been equally abundant about 6,600 million years ago. If it is assumed that the odd isotope was never the more abundant, then this result provides a significant estimate for the age of terrestrial uranium. This estimate corresponds to what may be called a 'single event' synthesis. Recently, an alternative possibility has been suggested: uranium may have been produced in a uniform series of supernovae explosions occurring between the formation of the Galaxy and the time of formation of the protostar from which the Sun condensed. Calculations show that this process would have ended about 5,000 million years ago and would have begun some time between 6,600 and 11,500 million years ago. Taking 10,000 million years as a round figure, it would follow that this is a rough estimate for the age of our Galaxy.

The radioactive method for determining the age of terrestrial rocks has an immediate bearing on the age of the Sun. The amount of radiation received from the Sun cannot have varied by more than a few per cent. at most since life has existed on Earth. The oldest fossils occur in Cambrian rocks which are estimated to be some 500 million years old. Hence, the Sun must have been in much the same state for that interval of time. We have already seen that gravitational contraction provides an inadequate source for solar energy, and *a fortiori* chemical combustion is also ruled out since it can be calculated that, if the Sun were composed of an ideal mixture of coal and oxygen for complete combustion, its whole mass would be consumed in under 2,000 years.

The solution to the problem of the source of the Sun's energy was discovered only after the rise of nuclear physics, but it also depended on Eddington's theory of stellar structure. Eddington discovered that a star must be regarded as a huge ball of gas and that, in order to prevent it from collapsing rapidly under its own gravitational attraction, this force must be balanced by internal pressure which, in the case of a gas, can be sufficient only if the temperature increases very considerably towards that centre. The surface temperature of the Sun is deduced from observation to be nearly 6,000 degrees Centigrade. According to present views it must be about 20 million degrees at the centre. In his original researches Eddington was ignorant not only of the source of stellar energy but also of the detailed chemical composition of the stars. Not until the pioneer work of Rutherford and his colleagues was the possibility of nuclear reactions and transformations as sources of stellar energy envisaged.

An essential factor leading to a solution of the problem was the recognition of the key role played by the simplest and lightest of all elements, hydrogen. When Eddington was developing his theory the prevalent view seemed to be that stellar energy must be due primarily to some kind of natural radioactivity which is normally associated with the heavier elements. In the nineteen-thirties, however, astrophysicists discovered that stars such as the Sun are composed predominantly of hydrogen, and so it became evident that the nuclear transformations which might give rise to the observed stellar luminosities must be primarily syntheses of heavier elements rather than disintegrations. As everyone knows today, energy is released when light elements, such as hydrogen, are fused into heavier ones. This is due to the fact that in the process of fusion a small quantity of mass is converted into energy, one gramme giving rise to about 20 billion calories in accordance with Einstein's relation $E = Mc^2$. In particular, a large amount of energy is released if hydrogen is converted into the next lightest element, helium, which has a very stable nucleus. For the maintenance of such a reaction, unlike radioactive disintegration of the heaviest elements, a very high temperature of the order of millions of degrees is necessary. Since, as already mentioned, temperatures of this order are believed to occur in the central regions of the Sun and stars, it follows that we may expect such thermonuclear reactions (as they are called) to occur there.

In 1938 Bethe suggested two possible processes which have come to be known as the hydrogen chain and the carbon cycle. Each of these processes results in the synthesis of helium from hydrogen, but the latter depends on the presence of carbon which functions as a catalyst. Which of these two processes operates in a particular star depends on various conditions, particularly its size. These thermonuclear reactions are extremely sensitive to changes in temperature. As a result, energy production in a star is strongly concentrated towards its centre. We believe that in the case of the Sun the temperature near the centre is just high enough for the conversion of hydrogen into helium to proceed very slowly so that the Sun remains in nearly the same state for thousands of millions of years. When first proposed it was thought that the carbon cycle was the predominant source of the Sun's energy, but in recent years astrophysicists have come to the conclusion that the hydrogen chain, which begins to operate significantly at a temperature of about 5 million degrees, is more important, the carbon cycle being the chief source in somewhat larger stars with higher central temperatures.

The tremendous scale on which the solar furnace operates results in the conversion every second of some 800 million tons of hydrogen into helium. At this rate it would take some 50,000 million years for the total conversion of the Sun's hydrogen. As it is believed that not much mixing of matter occurs outside the central regions, it follows that only a fraction—that nearer the centre—is likely to be converted and so the total period may be of the order of 10,000 million years. Calculations indicate that the Sun has consumed about half its available hydrogen, in which case its present age is roughly 5,000 million years. This result depends on a number of assumptions, notably the hypothesis that Eddington's *mass-luminosity law*,[1] according to which the stars of greater mass are those of greater luminosity, those of smaller mass of fainter luminosity, applies throughout. Consequently, since a star loses only a fraction of a per cent. of its mass during the conversion of its hydrogen into helium, it radiates at the same rate all the time.

Although the range in stellar masses is believed to be very restricted (nearly[2] all lie between two-fifths and four times the mass of the Sun), the range in stellar luminosities is far greater, and the brightest stars must therefore be radiating prodigally by comparison. Not all stars conform to Eddington's law, but the life-expectancy at its present rate of radiation of a typical bright star which does, Capella,[3] is only about 20 million years. Indeed, some Population I

[1] For stars obeying this law, luminosity depends mainly on mass. Red giants (very large diameters) and white dwarfs (very small diameters) are exceptions.

[2] Nevertheless, despite their extreme rarity, stars heavier than ten solar masses may provide nearly half the total *bolometric* luminosity of all stars in the Sun's neighbourhood and most of the ultraviolet radiation.

[3] It is in fact a double star, but its two components are very similar in their physical properties.

stars have even shorter life-expectancies of the order of only a million years and therefore must have been formed very recently. It is highly probable that stars like these are still being formed in our part of the Milky Way. For the emergence of new stars we must look to the thickest dusty regions, e.g. the great cloud complex in Orion. It is significant that the highly luminous blue and bluish-white (O and B) stars occur in those regions of our Galaxy where interstellar gas and dust are plentiful.

On the other hand, the most prominent Population II stars are under-luminous as compared with stars of equivalent masses obeying the mass-luminosity law. For, although very few masses are known for stars of Population II (because double stars of this type in our galactic neighbourhood appear to be rarer than those of Population I), it is possible to infer the mass of a star, such as Arcturus, from its spectral peculiarities. Since it is a high-velocity star, we believe it to be of Population II and similar to the red giants in globular clusters. We find that this star is distinctly underluminous for its mass, and this suggests that, compared with stars of Population I, those of Population II are, in general, less prodigal radiators. This would account for the fact that the brightest Population II stars are several magnitudes fainter than the brightest of Population I.

Broadly speaking, this line of argument points to the conclusion that the brighter (and, therefore, more readily detectable) stars of Population II are older than those of Population I. Consequently, if we are studying star formation in the Galaxy at the present time we must concentrate on the latter, whereas if we want to estimate the probable age of the Milky Way we must turn our attention to systems of Population II stars, in particular to globular clusters.[1] With the 200-inch telescope detailed study of those remarkable objects has been greatly facilitated. For the first time it has become possible to observe in the nearer clusters stars which are known to obey Eddington's mass-luminosity law.

If the spectral classes (temperatures or colours) of stars obeying this law are plotted against their absolute magnitudes, the points are all found to lie within a fairly narrow band known as the *Main Sequence*. This was first established in 1913 by Russell of Princeton following a preliminary indication by Hertzsprung of Leiden. The

[1] See, however, the discussion of M67 on p. 184.

terms *H-R diagram* and *colour-magnitude diagram* are used to denote a graph of this type for *any* system of stars. The colour-magnitude diagrams for globular clusters are found to differ from the main sequence band characterizing the stars in our part of the Milky Way (predominantly Population I). Roughly speaking, the main sequence band is a diagonal path running from faint-and-red to bright-and-blue. Globular cluster stars, however, although merging with the main sequence at the faint (and red) end tend, as we pass to brighter and brighter stars, to branch off[1] away from the blue (high surface temperature) and towards the red (lower surface temperature). Different globular clusters yield similar diagrams.[2] The position of the turn-off point is believed to be a measure of the age of a cluster. For, as the brighter stars convert their available hydrogen into helium so they move off the main sequence, slowly at first and then with increasing rapidity.[3] The discovery that in some globular clusters the branch point of main sequence stars occurs at absolute magnitude 3·5 has led theoretical investigators to assign an age of about 5,000 million years to these clusters. This result has been broadly confirmed by independent calculations on the evolutionary tracks of Population II stars (*see* Fig. II).

Recently the first colour-magnitude diagram for an elliptical nebula has been obtained. It is similar to that for a typical globular cluster and therefore provides evidence that all the stars in this galaxy were formed some five or six thousand million years ago. Indeed, Baade goes further and asserts that there must have been a period of star formation in all galaxies at about that epoch. In the

---

[1] As already mentioned, the most luminous stars of Population II are red, whereas those of Population I are blue and bluish-white.

[2] *See* the tracks for M3 and M92 in Fig. I.

[3] Although the mode of evolution away from the main sequence is not yet known, it is thought that the helium core cools as the hydrogen fuel is used up. The pressure consequently falls and gravitational contraction occurs. This leads to a sudden rise in temperature—to 100 million degrees or more—and this rise allows thermonuclear reactions in helium to occur. The outer envelope of the star becomes heated and expands enormously. The large surface radiates cooler, i.e. redder, light, and the star has become a red giant. Incidentally, it was pointed out by Öpik in 1938 and also by Hoyle and Lyttleton in 1942 that a chemically inhomogeneous star with a discontinuity of mean molecular weight in the interior (i.e. a star in which 'mixing' has not occurred on a large scale) will have a larger radius than a chemically homogeneous star of the same mass.

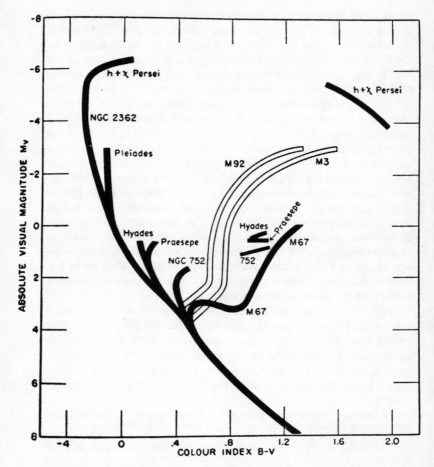

FIG. I. Comparison of the colour-magnitude diagrams for seven galactic clusters and two globular clusters M3 and M92. (Colour index B—V indicates temperature, maximum on the left.)

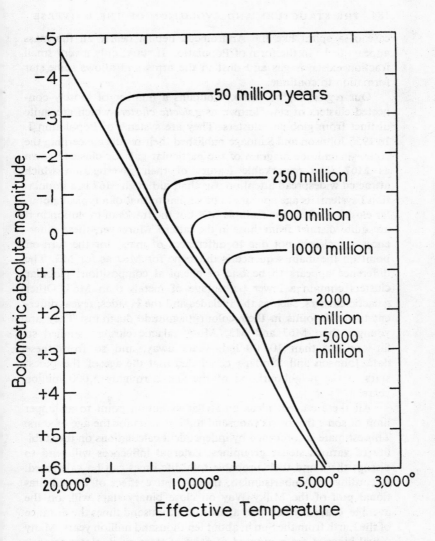

FIG. II. Theoretical colour-magnitude diagrams for galactic clusters of different ages. (It is assumed that the stars originated on the main-sequence shown on the left. A scarcity of stars is predicted beyond the respective 'turn-off' points.)

case of a spiral like the Andromeda nebula nearly all the mass appears to be in the form of Population II stars; only a very small fraction exists as gas and dust in the arms and allows some star formation to continue.

Our region of the Galaxy contains a number of loosely connected clusters of stars known as *galactic clusters* which are quite distinct from globular clusters. They are systems of Population I. In 1955 Johnson and Sandage published their results concerning the colour-magnitude diagram of the particular galactic cluster known as M67. The remarkable feature of their investigation which attracted widespread attention was that, although M67 is a Population I system, its age appears to be similar to that of a typical globular cluster, such as for example M3, but the tracks of evolution in it are quite distinct from those in the latter.[1] Moreover, these differences are clearly not due to differences of mass, for the turn-off point on the main sequence is the same for M67 as for M3. The difference appears to be one of chemical composition: globular clusters contain a lower percentage of metals than M67. Other galactic clusters, such as the Pleiades and the Hyades, reveal different turn-off points in their colour-magnitude diagrams. They are younger than M67 and M3. Most galactic clusters studied so far are less than 10,000 light-years away, and so from these data Johnson and Sandage concluded that the age of the oldest stars in the neighbourhood of the Sun is roughly 5,000 million years.

All these current ideas on stellar evolution point to an upper limit of some five or six thousand million years for the age of stars. This estimate is confirmed by independent calculations on the stability of various stellar groupings. External influences will tend to disrupt them and their probable total life-times can be calculated. According to Ambartsumian, the disruptive effect of the gravitational pull of the Milky Way on close binary stars will, on the average, draw a typical pair apart to ten thousand times the distance of the Earth from the Sun in about ten thousand million years. Many visual binaries are composed of pairs of stars much closer to each other than this. Since we believe that a considerable proportion of stars belong to such systems, we infer that the disruptive influence

[1] *See* Fig. I.

of the Galaxy cannot have been acting for longer than about 10,000 million years.

This disruptive influence of the Galaxy also tends to tear apart loose clusters of stars. It has been found that clusters of this type fall into two classes according as their density is less than, or exceeds, a certain critical value depending on the distance of the cluster from the centre of the Galaxy and to a lesser extent on its shape. For spherical clusters whose distance from this centre is comparable with the Sun's, the critical density is of the order of three stars of the mass of the Sun in a volume equal to that of a cube of side ten light-years. If the star-density is lower, then the cluster will be unstable and will disintegrate rapidly. If the star-density is greater, we can regard the cluster as stable, the rate of dissolution being much slower. The estimated density of the Hyades cluster is about two and a half times the critical density, and it has been calculated that its lifetime is of the order of 2,000 million years. During that period the probable number of encounters with other stars will have reduced the system to a state in which the Galactic pull can tear it apart.

The mechanism of disintegration of dense star clusters is quite different. In galactic clusters like the Pleiades, the density of which exceeds the critical density by a factor of more than five, the pull of the Galaxy is no longer the dominant disruptive influence. Instead the gradual impoverishment of these clusters is mainly due to the gravitational interaction between member stars. Associated with any gravitational system there is at each point a definite velocity of escape. If a particular star in a cluster has a particular velocity, we can calculate the probability that this star will acquire the velocity of escape within a given interval of time. Stars acquiring this velocity will ultimately leave the system. The remaining stars will have somewhat reduced average energy and consequently will not move quite so far from the centre of the cluster as before. The cluster will therefore not only become depleted with the passage of time but will also tend to collapse on itself. The predicted times in which collapse should take place are of the order of a few thousand million years.

Recently, however, Oort has drawn attention to the fact that, although the rate of creation of galactic clusters which are less than 500 million years old appears to be uniform, there is a marked deficiency of older clusters. In 1957 he suggested that some process leads to the disintegration of these clusters within 1,000 million years of formation. In an important paper published in 1958, Spitzer has calculated that the disruptive effect of close encounters with interstellar clouds, which he maintains is far more effective than with field stars, could produce the required results. From his calculations he claims that the Hyades cluster is liable to disruption in this way within 60 million years, the Pleiades cluster may survive for up to 1,000 million years, but only a comparatively dense galactic cluster such as M67 can survive for 5,000 million years. But, as Spitzer himself has remarked, a more detailed comparison of his theory with observation is required before it can be regarded as established.

Although these investigations all yield ages of the order of a few thousand million years at most, at one time many astronomers believed that important arguments based on observational evidence indicated that our stellar system must be a thousand times older than this. This 'long' time-scale, of the order of a million million to ten million million years, was based primarily on the researches of Jeans. One of the arguments on which Jeans laid considerable stress concerned the observed approximation to *equipartition of energy* among the stars. In 1911 Dr. Halm of the Cape Observatory correlated the average velocities of stars of various spectral types with their average weights or masses. He showed that for most types the product of their average weight and the square of their average velocity is the same. This product is proportional to the kinetic energy of the star. There is a famous law due to Maxwell which states that in a mixture of two or more gases there will be equipartition of energy, the heavier molecules moving more slowly than the lighter ones. Moreover, if the gases are suddenly mixed together in a vessel, it is possible to calculate the total time required for equipartition to occur. Halm's result suggested that the stellar system could be regarded as a gas in which the stars play the part of molecules. Given an initial random distribution of motion among the stars it should be possible to calculate the length of time needed for gravitational forces to speed up the slow stars and to slow down the fast stars until equipartition is observed. According to Jeans the required period is from five to ten million million years.

This calculation was based on the assumption that the observed approach to equipartition was due to the effect of stars passing close to each other. In recent years reasons have been advanced for doubting whether, in fact, the observed trends towards equipartition are sufficient to indicate that stellar encounters have been causing them over an interval of the order of 10 million million years. For the trend towards equipartition should be universal, whereas there are important deviations. Moreover, in all arguments concerning equipartition the velocities of the stars must be determined with respect to a definite standard frame of reference. In practice we begin by measuring their velocities relative to the Sun and then we correct for the effect of the Sun's local motion, i.e. its motion relative to the stars in its vicinity. But since Halm's pioneer investigation it has been found that the Galaxy rotates. Consequently, the velocities of the stars should be referred to the centre of galactic rotation because the Sun's local motion is less significant than its motion with respect to this centre. The problem of equipartition is now seen to depend on the observed correlations of the physical properties of stars and their orbital characteristics in the Galaxy. Much still remains to be done concerning such correlations, but according to Bok we may 'state with confidence that the equipartition argument can no longer be quoted in support of the long time scale'.

Just as we study clusters of stars in order to compute probable ages and life-expectancies, similarly we can investigate clusters of galaxies. By comparing the respective red-shifts of the members of a cluster, we can estimate their relative motions and hence compute the time for which the cluster will be likely to hold together under the mutual gravitational attraction of its parts. Some of the largest clusters have life expectancies of 10,000 million years. The fact that so many clusters of galaxies are still observed suggests that their ages may be somewhat less than this.

These clusters may hold the ultimate key to the great problem of the age of the universe, which is intimately connected with the problem of its basic structure. For, if the universe is expanding, then it can only have existed in its present state for a finite time, although the actual measure of this time will depend on whether the recession of the galaxies is approximately uniform or was different in the past. In the former case the time that has elapsed since expansion began, according to the latest value assigned to Hubble's 'constant', is of the order of roughly fourteen thousand million years. If expansion is slower now than in the past, the time since expansion began may be some eight or nine thousand million years. If, however, the universe is in a steady-state, with new clusters of galaxies continually being formed as older ones move away from each other, then the total range of past time must be *infinite*. We have already seen, in Chapter 5, that an ambitious but laborious statistical programme has been formulated to determine whether the observed spatial distribution of clusters of galaxies—the largest of all identifiable groups of physical objects—accords with the steady-state hypothesis or whether it indicates that the universe itself changes with the passage of time. So far no definitive results have been obtained. In the last few years, however, another and more dramatic method of deciding between the two basic hypotheses has been suggested.

This method concerns phenomena associated with the collision of two galaxies in a cluster. There is now abundant photographic evidence that such collisions occur (*see* Plate VIII). Theoretical investigation has shown that two galaxies can interpenetrate and pass through each other with no appreciable effect on the stars in either system, except for some perturbation of their motions and spatial arrangement. The main result of a nebular collision, whether total or partial, will be to heat the gas and dust in either system to a high temperature (possibly millions of degrees) and sweep this diffuse matter away into outer space. In general, collisions will only be partial, and a galaxy will have to experience a fairly large number before it loses all its interstellar matter. In a comparatively dense cluster such as the Coma cluster, in the central part of which some 500 nebulae are concentrated in a region less than 3 million light-years in diameter, a galaxy moving roughly along a line through the centre of the system would have experienced in the course of 5,000 million years between five and thirty collisions depending on its size. These would have removed nearly all the interstellar matter from most members of this cluster.[1]

[1] Before an actual instance of this type of phenomenon had been observed, Baade and Spitzer had postulated nebular collisions in order to account for the curious fact that most of the galaxies in the Coma cluster have the general form of spirals—notably a flattened discoidal shape—but

In 1951 radio-astronomers at Cambridge isolated a very strong radio source, called Cygnus A, within an area of less than one square minute of arc. This region was then photographed by Baade with the 200-inch reflector on Mount Palomar who found to his surprise that what had previously appeared on plates taken with less powerful telescopes to be a single nebula was in fact a pair of interpenetrating galaxies. Study of the spectrum of Cygnus A confirmed this collision theory, for it showed that almost half of the light of the system is in broadened lines of hydrogen and lines of emission by other elements in highly ionized states indicative of very high temperatures. Incidentally, it was possible to measure the red-shift[1] and hence, by Hubble's law, to assign to these colliding galaxies a distance of about 300 million light-years.

This discovery led to a search for further identifications of so-called *radio-stars* with colliding galaxies. A few more have been found, notably the object known to astronomers as NGC 1275, the brightest member of a cluster of galaxies in Perseus. Careful analysis of its spectrum yields convincing evidence that it is composed of a tightly wound spiral in collision with an open spiral with distorted arms. From this and other evidence it is clear that strong radio emission occurs only when galaxies actually penetrate each other, although the precise mechanism which generates this radiation is still uncertain. We believe that this radiation cannot be due solely to the heating of the gas as a result of the collision, for in Cygnus A the rate of emission of radio energy is about ten times that of the visible radiation. It is probable that part at least of this immense outpouring of energy is due to the motion of high energy electrons in a weak magnetic field, a process which has been observed in a very strong radio source inside the Milky Way—the Crab nebula which

lack both the arms and the clouds of gas which are normally found in systems of this type. Spitzer and Baade argued that these *SO* galaxies were originally spirals, but that successive close encounters had deprived them of their clouds of gas and dust in which the highly luminous stars characteristic of spiral arms are generated. This explanation is further confirmation of the theory that in the spiral arms gas and dust, rather than stars, are primary and that without this diffuse matter these arms cannot be formed.

[1] This was the source, mentioned in Chapter 5, for which the Doppler shift of the 21-centimetre radio line agreed with that of lines in the optical spectrum.

is believed to be a product of the supernova explosion observed by the Chinese in 1054.

The identification of strong extragalactic radio sources with colliding galaxies opened up an exciting new vista for research into the depths of the universe. For it offered the prospect of extending our view even beyond the limits of the Mount Palomar telescope and of obtaining information of a kind that could not be revealed by an optical instrument. Extragalactic radio-sources of the intensity of Cygnus A are extremely rare—perhaps one for every hundred million normal galaxies—but Ryle and his colleagues at Cambridge have discovered nearly two thousand. The fact that they are distributed more or less equally all over the sky (except for that part which cannot be observed from Cambridge) is compatible with the identification of most of them as extragalactic, although it is conceivable that we might be surrounded in all directions by hitherto undetected sources in our own Galaxy. The most remarkable result of this survey was Ryle's claim, in 1955, that the number of sources detected by his radio-telescope increases more rapidly with distance than would be expected if they were distributed uniformly throughout space. If these radio-stars lie within the Milky Way, we must be in a region where they are rare, and the number per unit volume of space must increase with distance. But in that case their aggregate radiation is such that they would have to occupy a large part of our Galaxy, in which case we should expect them to be distributed most thickly in the neighbourhood of the main plane and not isotropically. A more consistent picture arises if we assume that most of the sources are extragalactic objects comparable with Cygnus A and extending to distances at which they are not optically detectable with present instruments. (Owing to the comparatively slow variation of the radio emission with wave-length, the red-shift has a much smaller effect on *intensity* than in the case of light.)

Ryle's conclusion that there is a marked excess of faint sources compared with the number that would be expected if the distribution in space were uniform has since been challenged by the Australian radio-astronomers. If, however, further surveys confirm the extragalactic origin of most radio-stars, then Ryle believes that their distribution in space will yield a powerful criterion for deciding between evolutionary and steady-state theories of the universe. For, if most of the radio-stars are pairs of colliding galaxies, the variation of their number with distance will be a measure of the frequency of nebular collisions.[1] The signals which we are now receiving originated hundreds and even thousands of millions of years ago. If the number of radio-stars *per unit volume of space* increases with distance, this will be evidence that encounters between galaxies were more frequent then than now, and consequently will indicate that the universe was denser in the past and therefore has been expanding. If, however, the universe is in a steady state, the average number of collisions per unit volume should not change significantly with time. Thus, if Ryle's views[2] are ultimately confirmed, these radio-surveys may provide powerful evidence that the universe is expanding and that its age is therefore finite.

Although we have no final and compelling proof of the finite range of past time, many independent lines of inquiry into the history of the Earth, the stars and the galaxies converge in a remarkable manner towards eras in the past of the order of five to fifteen thousand million years ago. Each of these methods of dating involves an enormous extrapolation from present observations. None can be regarded as providing conclusive evidence, but together they strongly suggest that the universe has a finite age of this order of magnitude, unless it is continually replenishing itself with new matter as in the steady-state theory. Various theories of the initial state of the universe have been formulated by theoretical cosmologists. According to Eddington, the world began as an unstable Einstein universe. According to Lemaître, it originated with the explosion of an enormous radioactive super-atom and later passed slowly through the unstable Einstein state and then continued to expand in the manner envisaged by Eddington as cosmical repulsion overcame gravitational attraction. Dispensing with the idea of repulsion, and regarding the average net effect of world-

---

[1] It should, however, be mentioned that the basis of Ryle's own analysis is that the intensity of a source decreases with the square of the distance. *This presupposes that space is effectively Euclidean.* His results would be modified if the curvature is not zero. They might be regarded as evidence that space is hyperbolic.

[2] In his Royal Society Bakerian Lecture, published in November 1958, he maintains his claim that 'there appears to be a real discrepancy between the observations and the predictions of the steady-state model.'

gravitation on a typical nebula or cluster as zero (because of isotropy), Milne introduced the attractive idea of uniform expansion but boldly coupled this with a curious belief that the world originated at a point-source.

Neither Eddington nor Milne propounded any detailed theory of the various forms and configurations of matter which we find in the universe. Such cosmogonical questions have been considered by others, notably Lemaître and Gamow. Lemaître's theory provides an explanation for the origin of heavy elements and cosmic rays but cannot account for the generation of the lighter elements. On the other hand, the theory developed by Gamow and his collaborators fails to explain the generation of heavy elements. According to this theory, the universe began as a hot nuclear gas at a temperature of thousands of millions of degrees so that all matter was in the form of the simplest particles: protons, neutrons and electrons, but principally neutrons because under the great pressure electrons would be pressed into the protons. Owing to expansion, this gas became both less dense and much cooler, and neutrons adhered to protons (formed from the decay of neutrons) to produce complex nuclei, the prototypes of the atomic nuclei with which we are familiar today.

The principal difficulty of Gamow's theory arises as a direct consequence of the fact that it entails a step-by-step process of successive neutron capture to build up the more complex nuclei from the simplest. Unfortunately, neither a single proton nor a single neutron can be attached to the helium nucleus, of mass 4, to obtain the next isotope of mass 5. There is in nature no isotope of mass 5, and although it has been produced artificially in the laboratory by bombarding helium-4 with neutrons, it immediately breaks down to helium-4 again. Hence, to build up an isotope of mass 6, two particles must be captured simultaneously by a helium nucleus, but under the assumed physical conditions the probability of this happening is negligibly small. This failure of Gamow's theory to account for the existence in nature of the heavier elements is, however, less serious than the failure of Lemaître's theory to account for the lighter elements because the lightest element of all—hydrogen —is by far the most abundant in the universe. Gamow himself now agrees that the heavy elements may well have been formed later in the hot interiors of stars. Indeed, Hoyle has shown how, in the interior of a star with a hot core of helium at a temperature of 100 million degrees, nuclei of mass 8 (which are also highly unstable and as ephemeral as those of mass 5) can be produced *at as fast a rate as they decay*. It is therefore possible from time to time for such a nucleus to fuse with a helium-4 nucleus to produce carbon-12. Hoyle found that a carbon-12 nucleus generated in this way would have to have certain peculiar properties. Subsequent laboratory experiments have shown that carbon can in fact exist in the required state. Although further arguments are required to account for the generation of the other elements, the main hurdle seems to have been surmounted. That the stars do in fact synthesize heavy elements has been confirmed observationally in various ways. The most remarkable evidence concerns the unstable element technetium. Its longest-lived isotope has a half-life of just over 200,000 years—far less than the age of the stars in which its spectral lines have been observed. To exist in a significant quantity this element must therefore have been generated in the star long after the star itself was formed.

Despite conflicting views concerning the origin of matter and the expansion of the universe, most astronomers agree that the galaxies must have condensed out of a dilute and turbulent expanding gas. The possible course of subsequent events has been outlined by Oort, who is generally recognized as one of the world's leading authorities on the structure of our own and other galaxies. Despite general expansion, there must have been places where gravitational attraction was so strong that it overcame the tendency to expand. In this way, separate aggregates of matter detached themselves from the rest of the universe, forming protogalaxies which contracted under their own gravitation. As they did so, collisions of the component gas currents became more frequent and led to further contraction. For, as the result of such collisions, much of the kinetic energy of these currents was converted into heat and radiated away, thus gradually reducing the intended motions of the protogalaxy. Contraction was, however, limited by two important factors. A process similar to the formation of protogalaxies led to the formation of protostars inside them, and this tendency for gas to condense into separate globules greatly reduced the likelihood of collisions. Also, just as eddies are formed when currents of water meet, so the intermingling of the primeval gas currents presumably must have often given rise to rotation. As a rotating protogalaxy continued to contract, so its rate of spin would increase, its axis of rotation remaining unchanged according to the principle of the conservation of angular momentum. This would in turn lead to an increase in centrifugal force until it balanced gravitational attraction. The system would then cease to contract in the plane of rotation (perpendicular to the axis), although contraction would still continue towards this plane from 'above' and 'below'.

This theory provides a plausible explanation of the sharp dichotomy between the disc-shaped spirals and the more globular elliptical galaxies. By a well-known theorem of dynamics a system in rotation about an axis tends to become disc-shaped with its main plane perpendicular to the axis of rotation, this tendency being the stronger the greater the angular momentum or spin. Thus, a protogalaxy would become disc-shaped and contraction in the plane of rotation would be severely limited. Consequently, the mean density in this main plane would be low and much gas in it would remain uncondensed, especially towards the periphery. On the other hand, a slowly spinning protogalaxy would be dominated by gravitational attraction towards its centre of mass and so would be spheroidal and would ultimately become a comparatively dense system completely condensed into stars.

One of the most exciting features of this general theory of nebular evolution is the light it throws on the origin of Baade's two stellar populations.[1] We have already seen that, broadly speaking, Population II stars are old, whereas the more prominent members of Population I are not. According to the present theory, stars of Population II type may have been formed in the earliest stages, possibly even before a protogalaxy became separated from the rest of the universe. This system of very old stars—including those in globular clusters—was not spinning rapidly enough to contract to a

---

[1] In recent years, however, it has become apparent, e.g. following the discovery of systematic spectral differences between globular clusters and groups of stars in the disc, that Baade's original division of a spiral like the Milky Way into two distinct populations needs to be refined. Five divisions, forming a continuous sequence, have been suggested: Halo Population II; Intermediate Population II; Disc Population; Intermediate Population I; Extreme Population I.

disc but instead became a comparatively spherical group concentrated towards the centre of the protogalaxy, although as the latter fell in towards its main plane of rotation many of these Population II stars were left behind and tended to move around the centre in nearly circular orbits steeply inclined to the main plane, or disc. In the disc itself the oldest stars formed are now so old that we regard them as Population II stars, but in the large quantities of gas that remained Population I stars have been generated for thousands of millions of years up to the present day.

So far the main shortcoming of this attractive theory is its failure to account for the creation of spiral arms, but this does not mean that the theory as so far described may not be substantially correct. As already indicated in Chapter 7, however, it is becoming clear that these arms, although picturesque, are only secondary and evanescent features of the systems in which they are found. The highly luminous O and B stars which dominate them were probably formed less than 50 million years ago. They may be regarded as tracing out the instantaneous spiral arms and their motions. Astronomers hope that, if they can succeed in identifying a group of somewhat older stars with ages up to about 200 million years, and can obtain information concerning their spatial distribution and motion, much might then be learned about the form of the spiral arms at the time when these stars originated.

However great the difficulties to be overcome before we can account for the creation of these fascinating but puzzling structures, the great problem of the origin of the whole universe is likely to remain far more elusive. Although this is perhaps the oldest of the traditional problems of speculative philosophy, progress towards its solution was slow and halting until the scientific revolution of the seventeenth century. Nevertheless, despite the powerful tools supplied to him by modern physics, the theoretical cosmologist unlike most of his scientific colleagues cannot so easily cast off the shackles of metaphysics. His subject is still regarded by many as primarily a form of philosophical speculation. To some extent this is inevitable. At the beginning of this book, I drew attention to a remark by Pascal on the incompleteness of our observational knowledge of the universe: 'But if our view be arrested there let our imagination pass beyond.' More recently, de Sitter reminded us that 'the universe is a hypothesis'. From the point of view of the physical scientist everything outside the region of observation in space and time is pure extrapolation. The pendulum has swung to the opposite extreme since philosophers first sought the essential nature of the world in pure thought: in recent years serious doubts have been raised not merely about the answers to basic cosmological questions, but about the propriety of asking them. In particular, the very *meaning* of the idea that the universe has a finite age has been challenged. It has been argued that the mere fact that the steady-state universe of continual creation is ageless is *ipso facto* a compelling criterion in its favour.

Now, it must be admitted that many people are baffled by the idea of a first instant of physical time which seems to be implied by the concept of a limited past for the universe. Nevertheless, however puzzling this idea may seem, it is *not* meaningless. For example, we can imagine a first instant of time occurring in a perfectly homogeneous and static universe formed of identical particles in equilibrium when one of them spontaneously decays. Such a first instant would not necessarily be an instant of world-creation. It would be the beginning of time in the sense that it was the first thing that happened in the universe. Indeed, whereas the steady-state theory introduces the difficult concept of creation *ex nihilo* as a new law which operates simultaneously with the recognized laws of physics, evolutionary theories of the universe separate this idea of creation from physical events. A believer in world-evolution is not obliged to formulate any concept whatsoever of creation *ex nihilo*. For, strictly speaking, all that his interpretation of the phenomena compels him to accept is the idea that the total range of *past time* over which man can apply to the universe the laws of physics, is limited.

As for the total range of *future time*, it used to be the general view of most astronomers and physicists that the cosmos was tending towards a 'heat-death', owing to the universal degradation of energy. This conclusion was based on the assumption that the Second Law of Thermodynamics—the law of increasing entropy—could be *automatically* applied to the *whole universe*. In recent years there has, however, been a growing tendency to regard this assumption as unfounded, or at least as open to question, particularly in view of the fact that there is, as yet, no general agreement on whether the universe is finite or infinite, in process of evolution or in a steady state.

Our direct knowledge of the universe is inevitably so limited that, to obtain some idea of it as a whole, we must extrapolate far beyond the data accessible to observation. Looking out into the depths of space we see the Moon a little more than a second in time away, the Sun a few minutes, the nearest star a few years, the nearer nebulae hundreds of thousands of years, while radio-waves which we receive from the farthest perceptible galaxies have been travelling for several thousand million years. Judged by terrestrial standards, most of the intervening space is inconceivably empty, but at the limits of our vision there is still no sign of an end. Our idea of the universe as a whole remains a product of the imagination.

'. . . There was a monk indulging against the teaching of the Master in cosmological enquiries. In order to know where the world ends he began . . . interrogating the gods of the successive heavens. . . . Finally, the Great Brahma himself became manifest, and the monk asked him where the world ends. . . . The great Brahma took that monk by the arm, led him aside and said: "These gods, my servants, hold me to be such that there is nothing I cannot see, understand, realize. Therefore, I gave no answer in their presence. But I do not know where the world ends. . . ." '[1]

---

[1] *Dialogues of the Buddha.*

APPENDIX

WHY PHYSICAL SPACE HAS THREE DIMENSIONS

In Chapter 3 attention was drawn to the intimate connection between the predominating role played by the inverse square law in our analysis of the forces of nature (in particular gravitation) and the three-dimensional nature of physical space. Weyl has suggested that the geometrical peculiarities of three-dimensional space may lead to a reasonable explanation of the fact that the world has just this number of spatial dimensions. It is the purpose of this Appendix to outline a modified solution of this problem which I first published in 1955.

The key to this solution is provided by the fact that physical conditions on the Earth have been such that the evolution of Man has been possible. Is this possibility in any way dependent on the number of dimensions of physical space? Now, we know that the motion of the Earth about the Sun is *primarily* governed by the inverse square law of attraction and also that during the five hundred or more million years in which organic evolution has taken place the intensity of solar radiation on the Earth's surface cannot have fluctuated greatly. For, if it had, then higher forms of terrestrial life would have been destroyed and indeed might never have been possible. For this intensity to be approximately constant neither the Sun's rate of generation of radiation nor the Earth's distance from the Sun can have changed markedly during this immense period of time, since it is most improbable that a large variation in one would have been more or less compensated by any simultaneous variation in the other. Thus we believe that the Earth's distance from the Sun cannot have varied greatly, and we conclude that under prevailing conditions the Earth's orbit is not only very nearly circular but is also stable.

These considerations suggest that we examine the conditions

199

under which a circular, or nearly circular, orbit in the Sun's field of gravitational force can be stable, without imposing the customary condition that space is three-dimensional and hence that the orbital motion of the Earth is dominated by an inverse square law of force. Instead, let us merely postulate that the Earth describes a nearly circular orbit under the inverse s-th power law of force, appropriate to space of $n=s+1$ dimensions, and impose the condition that such an orbit is to be stable, so that as long as the Sun radiates steadily the intensity of radiation incident on the Earth's surface fluctuates little.

There is a well-known theorem of classical orbit theory which asserts that any circular, or nearly circular, orbit described in a central field of force with centre of orbit at centre of force is stable under a law of force proportional to the inverse s-th power of the distance if, and only if, s is less than three. The proof of this theorem makes no demands on the number of dimensions which we must assign to space, except that this number must be not less than two. (The third dimension, orthogonal to the plane of the orbit, and equally any conceivable additional dimensions, are irrelevant.) Since we clearly require $n = s + 1$ to be a positive whole number, it follows that under the conditions here imposed the only admissible values of n are $n = 1$, 2 or 3. We have thus discovered a possible criterion for eliminating all spatial dimensions *in excess of three*.

It is now necessary to invoke some argument for showing why the number of dimensions cannot be *less* than three. Following a suggestion due to Professor J. B. S. Haldane and a mathematical discussion with my colleague Mr. M. C. Austin, it seems to me that the solution to this problem lies in the geometrical structure of the human brain. This consists of a very large number of nerve-cells which can be connected in pairs in an immense number of ways to form neutral networks. Although one could imagine privacy preserved at a crossing by pairs of membranes with mutually exclusive permeabilities, arrangements of this type would become extremely complicated for the many billions of cells in question. In three or more dimensions any number of cells can be connected with each other in pairs without intersection of the joins, but in two dimensions the maximum number of cells for which this is possible is only four. *A fortiori* we can eliminate the case $n = 1$.

Thus, we may conclude that the number of dimensions of physical space is necessarily three, no more and no less, because it is the unique natural concomitant of the evolution of the higher forms of terrestrial life, in particular of Man, *the formulator of the problem.*

BIBLIOGRAPHY

(Abbreviations: *h* historical, *m* mathematical, *p* philosophical)

     Bok, B. J. and P. F., *The Milky Way*. Cambridge, Mass., Harvard University Press, 1957.

m   Bondi, H., *Cosmology*. Cambridge University Press, 1952.

     Borel, E., *Space and Time*. London and Glasgow, Blackie, 1931.

p   *British Journal for the Philosophy of Science*, 'Age of the Universe' Number, Vol. V, Nov. 1954.

     Couderc, P., *The Expansion of the Universe*. London, Faber, 1952.

h   de Sitter, W., *Kosmos*. Cambridge, Mass., Harvard University Press, 1932.

p   Dingle, H., *The Sources of Eddington's Philosophy*. Cambridge University Press, 1954.

h   Douglas, A. V., *The Life of Arthur Stanley Eddington*. Edinburgh, Nelson, 1956.

     Eddington, A. S., *Space, Time and Gravitation*. Cambridge University Press, 1920.

m   Eddington, A. S., *The Mathematical Theory of Relativity*. Cambridge University Press, 1922.

     Eddington, A. S., *The Expanding Universe*. Cambridge University Press, 1933.

m   Eddington, A. S., *Fundamental Theory*. Cambridge University Press, 1946.

     Einstein, A., *Relativity: the Special and the General Theory*. London, Methuen, 1955.

     Gamow, G., *The Birth and Death of the Sun*. New York, Macmillan, 1946.

     Gamow, G., *The Creation of the Universe*. New York, Macmillan, 1952.

Hoyle, F., *Frontiers of Astronomy*. London, Heinemann 1955.

Hubble, E. P., *The Realm of the Nebulae*. Oxford University Press, 1936.

Hubble, E. P., *The Observational Approach to Cosmology*. Oxford University Press, 1937.

h   Jammer, M., *Concepts of Space*. Cambridge, Mass., Harvard University Press, 1954.

Jones, G. O., J. Rotblat and G. J. Whitrow, *Atoms and the Universe*. London, Eyre and Spottiswoode, 1956.

h   Koyré, A., *From the Closed World to the Infinite Universe*. Baltimore, Johns Hopkins Press, 1957.

Lemaître, G., *L'Hypothèse de l'Atome Primitif*. Neuchâtel, Editions du Griffon, 1946.

Lovell, A. C. B., *The Individual and the Universe* (Reith Lectures). *The Listener*, November and December 1958.

McCrea, W. H., *Physics of the Sun and Stars*. London, Hutchinson University Library, 1950.

h   Macpherson, H., *Modern Cosmologies*. Oxford University Press, 1929.

m   McVittie, G. C., *General Relativity and Cosmology*. London, Chapman and Hall, 1956.

p   Mascall, E. L., *Christian Theology and Natural Science*. London, Longmans, 1956.

m   Milne, E. A., *Relativity, Gravitation and World-Structure*. Oxford University Press, 1935.

p   Milne, E. A., *Modern Cosmology and the Christian Idea of God*. Oxford University Press, 1952.

p   Munitz, M. K., *Space, Time and Creation*. Glencoe, Ill., The Free Press, 1957.

h   Munitz, M. K., *Theories of the Universe*. Glencoe, Ill., The Free Press, 1957.

Newton, H. W., *The Face of the Sun*. London, Pelican Books, 1958.

O'Connell, D. J. K. (ed.), *Stellar Populations*. North Holland Publishing Company, Amsterdam, 1958.

Payne-Gaposchkin, C., *Stars in the Making*. London, Eyre and Spottiswoode, 1953.

p   Reichenbach, H., *Space and Time* (trans. M. Reichenbach and
    J. Freund). London, Constable (Dover Publications), 1958.

    Schatzmann, E., *Origine et Evolution des Mondes*. Paris,
    Albin Michel, 1957.

    Scientific American, 'The Universe' Number (September
    1956). London, Bell, 1958.

    Shapley, H., *Galaxies*. London, Churchill, 1947.

h   Sidgwick, J. B., *William Herschel*. London, Faber, 1953.

h   Singer, D. W., *Giordano Bruno: his Life and Thought*.
    London, Constable, 1950.

m   Slater, N. B., *The Development and Meaning of Eddington's
    'Fundamental Theory'*. Cambridge University Press, 1957.

m   Tolman, R. C., *Relativity, Cosmology and Thermodynamics*.
    Oxford University Press, 1934.

    Whittaker, E. T., *The Beginning and End of the World*.
    Oxford Universtiy Press, 1942.

    Wright, H., *The Great Palomar Telescope*. London, Faber,
    1953.

    Zwicky, F., *Morphological Astronomy*. Berlin, Springer, 1957.

INDEX